Real to Re
Psychiatry at the cinema

Ron Roberts

PCCS BOOKS
Ross-on-Wye

First published 2011
Reprinted 2012

PCCS BOOKS
2 Cropper Row
Alton Road
Ross-on-Wye
Herefordshire
HR9 5LA
UK
Tel +44 (0)1989 763900
contact@pccs-books.co.uk
www.pccs-books.co.uk

Real to Reel: Psychiatry at the cinema

British Library Cataloguing in Publication Data.
A catalogue record for this book is available from the British Library.

ISBN 978 1 906254 42 1

Cover design by Old Dog Graphics
Printed by ImprintDigital.net, Exeter, UK

The institution of psychiatry like the institution of slavery, consists of a socially sanctioned relationship between a class of superiors coercively controlling a class of inferiors.

Thomas Szasz

Some might argue that what happened in Germany 60 years ago has nothing to do with how biological psychiatry operates today. We document these awful events, however, precisely because they so clearly illustrate, again, the three themes present throughout the history of the treatment of people considered mad: (1) social control in the interests of the powerful, (2) damaging and violent 'treatments', and (3) the ability of experts to generate theories camouflaging what is really happening.

John Read and Jeffrey Masson

For Russ

Contents

Acknowledgements

I'd like to begin by thanking Maggie and the team at PCCS Books for giving me the opportunity to do this book. I am particularly appreciative of the important role they play in disseminating ideas outside the mainstream and in so doing upholding a measure of academic freedom. Special thanks are due to Majda who has not only consistently supported me in writing this, but has given very generously of her valuable time, listening and discussing the contents. I have learnt an untold amount from her both from this and in many other ways. I am also indebted to Merry who has greatly assisted my endeavours by proofreading a fair bit of what's here. Needless to say any errors that remain are down to me. Thanks are again extended to Chris Hewer whose willingness to share ideas and engage in exploratory thinking make my working life so much better than it might otherwise be. As usual all my friends, by virtue of who they are, have contributed in unseen ways. Of these, Fergus, Arike, Delroi, Dave, Wandia and Subi deserve particular mention. Last though not least, I would like to thank my parents wholeheartedly for providing the building blocks and encouragement to be critical of what is going on around us. They are no longer here but their influence most definitely is.

Introduction: Psychiatry, the director's cut

The depiction of the wayward mind in motion pictures has a long history – in turn entertaining, frightening, shocking and provoking theatregoers – though seldom it must be said educating them. Akin to the worst excesses of the depiction of physical disability, those portrayed as mad have, more often than not, been fixed in the cinematic gaze as figures of horror, violence, pathos, fun or otherworldliness. This book however will not be a critical examination of the cinema's 'incorrect' and stereotyped depiction of the 'mentally ill' – the predominant means by which the relationship between the big screen and the wayward mind has hitherto been approached (Byrne, 2009). Such a perspective presumes the correctness of the disease model of mind and behaviour, taken as established fact in conventional psychiatric circles and by those who have previously enquired into psychiatry's relationship with the cinema. Gabbard and Gabbard (1999) for example see psychiatry's role to 'reconcile' the troubled to life in an unjust hierarchical society as unproblematic and axiomatic. For them pharmaceutical and physical methods used to bring about this 'readjustment' are 'impressive advances' (ibid: 143) in science. With such presumptions no critical examination of psychiatric power on screen worthy of the name can be possible. By way of contrast my point of departure in these critiques will be that the theory and practice of psychiatry represents a fundamentally mistaken, and harmful, approach to human well-being. In the course of examining the series of films discussed in these pages I hope to justify this stance. Nor in addition will this analysis presuppose the utility of always viewing the cinematic world through the framework of psychiatric or psychoanalytic theory, useful though the latter may sometimes be, and interesting. My central concern is with psychiatric reality and how the reality of psychiatric practice intrudes into the welcoming space of the big screen. The fantasies which support that reality are of course part of the story. Accordingly attention will fall upon the 'mad doctors' who inhabit the world of film, and more specifically the discipline and body politic of psychiatry which stands behind them. What follows is an exploration, through the camera lens, of psychiatry's relationship to those it deems of unsound mind, an exploration which will be conducted in the manner of an intellectual raid on the psychological foundations supporting the institution of psychiatry.

It is no accident that several of the films examined in this book are set in the 1950s and 1960s, a time of transition in the manifestation of the

American dream – then emerging into the steely light of cold war paranoia, and carrying within the Western psyche an unpalatable darkness that was the price of victory in the struggle with Nazism. The industrial and urban landscape of this period celebrated the triumph of a newly liberated though semiconscious capitalist reason. Beneath this lurked a submerged reality, unable in any direct way to break free from the confines of economic rationalism and articulate a truth at odds with the promises of everlasting progress in a modernist utopia. The subterranean and suppressed voices which spoke from this realm had a different message – alerting us to the excesses of both the market economy and the doctrines of reason, extolling not the virtues of the contemporary social and political order but its vices. The unwanted truth whispers that it is not, as Goya famously declared, the sleep of reason that threatens our ruination 'El sueño de la razón produce monstruos', but its very dreams – that is, it is the excesses of reason which have given birth to our nightmares[1] and this in the full light of day. It is surely no accident that as Fellini was heralding the demise of faith and the shallowness of La Dolce Vita, a parallel weakening of spiritual devotion and elevation of the beauty of the flesh, Thomas Szasz was furnishing the logical basis for the demise of psychiatric faith. Contemporaneously Ken Kesey and Janet Frame would provide further dramatic corpus delicti pertaining to psychiatry's crimes against the person whilst Hitchcock, peeling back the shower curtain in the Bates Motel would give us further evidence of modernity's ugly truth. As a bloody screaming Janet Lee entered cinematic history, the writing seemed to be on the wall not just for the purveyors of modern dreams but for those peddling psychological medicine as a cure-all for human ills.

This volume opens with an examination of Scorcese's Shutter Island which takes us further into the terra incognito of modernity's collapse. All is not what it seems as the apparent order of two US Federal Marshals investigating the disappearance of a female resident at a facility for the 'criminally insane' descends into a mélange of psychological breakdown, amidst intimations of state sponsored psychiatric torture. This provides our first glimpse into the ambiguities, confusion and heroics which typify public presentation of the psychiatric healer – simultaneously trusted and distrusted, at once feared yet still revered – part benevolent dictator, liberator, part tyrant, jailhouse keeper. The ambivalence which permeates our relationship to mental health professionals in their role as promulgators of state power are no better observed than as depicted here, as psychiatric interference moves from outright condemnation to enthusiastic endorsement. The multiplying realities unfolding before our eyes at first affirm the chief protagonist's insights as unsettling and true, before an

---

1. In Goya's native Spanish the phrase permits either interpretation.

insidious and wholesale takeover of the audience's will, propelled by an insistent and triumphant psychiatric benevolence, has them declared delusional and ergo consigned to memorial oblivion – for character, audience and writer alike. These are important clues here as to how and why the psychiatric project has managed to stay afloat. The Janus face of mental health care also looms large in the life of unconventional high school loner *Donnie Darko* who, in a parable of creation and destruction, must contend for his troubles with being drugged and psychoanalysed, while holed up in a community of would-be book burners; living cheek by jowl with classmates possessed of a *savoir-faire* for violence and cruelty and a local psychobabble guru with a private predilection for child pornography. Meanwhile there is the menacing hallucinatory presence of 'Frank', a giant rabbit prophesying the end of the world, instructing Donnie that he can do anything he wants. Like tightrope walker Philippe Petit, whose audacious high-wire walk across the twin towers of the World Trade Centre earned him a psychiatric arrest warrant – and that for the 'artistic crime of the century' (Marsh, 2008), Donnie must contend with society's intolerance toward those whose idiosyncrasies of thought and experience, whether grandiose or mundane, threaten a social order founded on loyalty to power, empty rules and regulations and a mission to seek out and destroy unrepentant psychiatric sinners.

But in all the works discussed here there is much more at stake than the dissolution and reconstitution of identity, the nature of sanity and the role of psychiatrists as healers or torturers. In presenting a version of the past through the medium of film, a vision of that past is at once revisited and recreated for mass consumption. These excursions into the re-remembered past – and the times considered here range from the 1920s to the 1980s – raise important questions regarding the events that get retained, distorted or deleted from the record prior to their re-presentation and assimilation to our ongoing common-sense history. For what purpose and with what consequences do these operations ensue? The social memory of psychiatry, and psychology for that matter as Read (2004a), Szasz (2007a), Harper (2007) and others have been at pains to remind us, is contested, rum-full of dark and not so delicious secrets. It is a reminder, were one needed – and it is, that the true point of psychiatry is not the spiritual edification of man, woman or child. The perennial issue of the persistence of the past can scarcely be avoided in any examination worth its salt of the historical presence of psychiatry on the silver screen. When it came to the imagining of the past in present hands, Orwell had much to say, not the least of which was that our political masters could 'make lies sound truthful and murder respectable, and … give an appearance of solidity to pure wind' (1946). We must ask whether our psychiatric masters are similarly learned, for if so what vestiges of truth can be discerned from the renderings of the dream factory when it cuts and pastes from the cloth of psychiatric history?

The contention of the various essays which follow is that some of this history is revealed in film – but as with the construction of all memory, whether individual or collective – the wholesale manufacture and fabrication of lies must also be reckoned with. If Hitchcock's *Spellbound* – released in the aftermath of World War II – is a sponsored paean to the power of psychoanalysis to combat insanity and restore reason to troubled minds, Ron Howard's *A Beautiful Mind* released in the aftermath of the September 11th attacks on New York provides us with a not so beautiful illustration of a still active resistance to exposing psychiatric brutalities at work in mainstream Hollywood. Here psychiatrists are 'knights of reason and order' saving the disturbed from the 'proliferating dragons of the mind' (Faggen, 2002: ix). These acts of heroism come to fruition in the former case through the hocus-pocus of Freudian detective work and in the latter through the long arm of the pharmaceutical industry, whose products are here credited with saving the mathematical abilities of game theorist turned 'schizophrenic' John Nash. If it were true that Nash was feasting on antipsychotics to save the engine of his reason, then it would also be true that his name would never have reached the Hollywood Hills for in all probability his brains would have been turned to something resembling psychological custard – an uncomfortable truth too many for the producers and aficionados of the film. Spellbound may well describe the mental stupefaction of those in the audience who chose to believe what they had just witnessed for the best part of two hours.

In any examination of psychiatry's relationship to those it manages one must inevitably contend with the exercise of power – by which one usually means its abuse. The subject is brought to the fore in Clint Eastwood's *Changeling* and Milos Forman's *One Flew Over the Cuckoo's Nest*. Eastwood's film addresses the combined judicial and psychiatric assault on one Christine Collins in 1920s Los Angeles, deemed unmanageable and delusional for her refusal to accept as her own an LAPD sponsored replacement who had arrived at her door purporting to be her missing (later discovered to have been murdered) son. Collins was forcibly incarcerated and then drugged, targeted for attack for the dual crimes of being female and independent, whereas fictional trickster Randall P. McMurphy's arrival at the mental hospital is all his own doing, a refugee he thinks from the drudgery of a prison 'work farm'. McMurphy's comic and increasingly desperate exhortations to his fellow inmates to claim their freedom and take back their lives from the power of Big Nurse are eventually brought to an unceremonial or might that be ceremonial lobotomous end. Forman's work is not as some would contend (e.g. Cox, 2010) a film about 'the mentally ill.' It is rather an exploration of how the mental health system, under the explicit imprimatur of the state, functions not only to destroy freedom of expression and cantankerous joyful rebellion but to also warn – those who currently lie beyond its grasping hands – that a prison awaits. It tells those whose lives do not meet the exacting standards of dull medically sanctioned normality – and that what lies in store should that test be failed is a fate that threatens not only the psychologically disturbed. If the psychological disintegration of US Marshal Teddy Daniels in *Shutter Island* could be said to progress through a maze of transcendent beauty, McMurphy's finale is transparent and brutal. These differences aside both tragedies are drunk with the Nietzschean overtones of psychiatrist as Übermensch. In 'O Superman', her melancholic hymn to the alienation and disconnection wrought by Big Science, Laurie Anderson intones 'when love is gone, there's always justice, and when justice is gone, there's always force'. McMurphy's functioning demise as a human being is crowned by the psychiatric powers, as an act of love. In the mental institution, justice is gone.

What follows then should not be read as a simple survey of celluloid insanity. The seven films which form the cornerstone of the text are used to examine psychiatry and psychiatric relationships in order to raise important questions about the public understanding and awareness of psychiatric power and practice. They also interrogate the role of the psychiatric profession in the social construction and manipulation of personal and social reality – the principal channels through which it functions as a vehicle for social control. The direction of the analytic journey is thus from the real to the reel. Inevitably within this review questions of what constitutes sanity and madness, truth and fantasy, reality and illusion, morality and immorality are never far from scrutiny. In the spirit of the times I have chosen to frame all such issues in the context of what is increasingly being recognised as a crisis in Western culture – as we witness a progressive decline in the ethical and modernist values which have shaped Western civilisation for centuries. Our diminishing confidence in grand narratives and economic and moral certainties arguably began before the Second World War but these have all certainly accelerated in the years after it. Psychiatry it might be argued stands as the definitive betrayal of the rationalist utopia, a proxy for the downturn in scientific dreams and faith in science. In its present guise it is a child of these heady times and psychiatry in the cinema provides a unique and telling account of just what is at stake.

Ron Roberts
London, May 2011

Chapter One

Shutter Island: History, memory and torture

A half century from now, people in the know will look back and say ... this is where it all began. The Nazis used Jews. The Soviets used prisoners in their own gulags. Here in America, we tested patients.

Rachel Solando (In Lehane, 2003: 306)

A preternatural world of dreamy fog greets a nauseated Teddy Daniels, bent double over a toilet bowl, unable to stomach the slow churning waters across which he is travelling, accompanying him his new partner Chuck Aule. They are two Federal Marshals on route to Shutter Island. An eerie cacophony of the ferry's warning siren pierces the unnatural calm amidst the gloom and with each wail of the horn the two sail further toward the cold dark heart of Ashecliffe Hospital, a facility for the 'criminally insane'. This is a journey into the white man's heart of darkness – into a territory that maps neither the imperial rape of Africa as depicted in Conrad's novel, nor the US destruction of South East Asia in Coppola's *Apocalypse Now*. 'Storm's coming' intones the ship's captain. We are closer to home – the 'light of civilisation' to be switched off this time will be courtesy of psychiatry, a specific brand of Western savagery.

Shutter Island can be read as an exploration of Western memory – or at least one part of it – in a century saturated with the moral failings of humanity. 'Welcome to Hell', scrawled on the city walls of Sarajevo greeted visitors to the Bosnian capital during the three-year siege (Vulliamy, 1994). This could well be the appropriate salutation to those about to set foot on Shutter Island. On the road to the hospital, escorted by cheerless gun-toting guards and jarring orchestral chords, Teddy and Chuck cast their eyes upon a plaque outside the hospital cemetery. The few words inscribed on it – 'Remember us for we too have lived, loved and laughed' – speak eloquently of the propensity to disregard the victims of the asylum system, whose lost and obliterated lives are a forgotten corner of our common humanity, sacrificed on the cold altar of a scientific materialism driven by the fever of professional passions. The Russell–Einstein manifesto implored us to 'remember your humanity and forget the rest', but as we now know this is not so easily done. The psychiatric hospital, from the birth of the asylum to the present, has by design been a place where the people in it are destined to be forgotten, programmed out of awareness by the shame and anger of the wider society and the closed mind of the professions.

The barbed wire mesh, that peculiarly twentieth century icon of atrocity that rings the hospital grounds, tells Teddy – a former World War II veteran, and us, if we care to remember, that the courtyards, wards and buildings they protect reverberate to the cultural memories of other twentieth century sites of horror. 'Seen something like it before,' he remarks to Chuck – and he has – in Dachau! His eyes are therefore ours. There is a certain irony, a knowing shock in this recollection – for symbols to be repeated which were the first time round so indelibly associated with the phrase 'never again' – purportedly first uttered by a Soviet officer commanding the liberating forces at Auschwitz. We now know with the cynicism that comes only from experience, that when the words are uttered by our political masters, they are an incantation to despotic power, an imperative command to 'never again' lose.

And so into the secure settings of the hospital; inmates in leg irons, wandering in a theatre of lost souls, engage in morning horticulture – these are the dangerous human 'failures' upon which psychiatrists practise their trade. The manacled and ageing bodies of the dispossessed wander before the incoming Marshals, conveying all the contradictions of coercive institutional psychiatry. Here its order is established before our eyes – confinement in chains supplemented no doubt by individual private 'treatment', or, as expressed for collective public consumption, the current fashion for restraint – be it chemical or physical – combined with a sheath of 'therapeutic benevolence'. It is for a good reason that psychiatry earned its label as the Cinderella of medicine – like Cinders, a squalid life went on behind closed doors, even if she did get to go to the ball for one night. And what goes on behind closed doors usually stays there, because no one is willing to believe it.

We are in 1954, on one of the Boston Harbour Islands, far from the public gaze. McCarthyism is in full swing, the American public swimming in the gloomy waters of state-directed anti-communist paranoia. The hospital has three wards, A for males, B for females, and C, reserved for the most dangerous 'patients' where entry is forbidden without the consent of the Warden and the man in charge, Dr Cawley. Cawley is introduced as a man revered amongst a host of international intelligence agencies – for his war work we are told. In response to Teddy's enquiry, Cawley describes the current work undertaken at the hospital as a 'moral fusion between law and order and clinical care', contrasting this with an open admission of the history of violence and torture administered to patients in past times by practitioners of his discipline in their 'honest' desire to 'drive ... psychosis out'. He says nothing of whether the desired ends justified the means, or what it means to build one's craft on such ignominy. He advocates trying to 'heal' and 'cure' and if that is not possible then to at least provide a 'measure of calm'. This serves to establish the credentials of Cawley as a humane man, a doctor not a torturer – one at odds with his discipline's past and a traveller on modernity's long road. He represents both a break with the past and a continuation of it. But like so much else in this film all is not what it seems. Amidst the litany of psychiatric cruelties recalled, from 'screws through the brain' to drowning patients, the evolution of psychiatry is presented as another step in the march of progress, part of the orderly transition from an ignorant ugly past, in which people under its jurisdiction were butchered and tormented, to an informed eternal future of humane scientifically based treatment. This is the modernist cloak of respectability psychiatry has worn ever since it took over the civic task of managing the asylums. Of insulin coma treatment, electroconvulsive therapy (ECT), or lobotomy, Cawley for the moment remains silent. Yet all of these 'treatments' were hugely popular with the profession and much in vogue in the mid-1950s. All of them offered a systematic, and some would say barbaric, means of damaging the grey matter, all were frequently employed against the wishes of the unfortunate recipients, and all lacked (and still do lack) credible scientific evidence to justify them (Moncrieff, 2008; Szasz, 2007a). The 'new' emerging post-war psychiatry then, putting aside its skirmishes with psychoanalysis, bathes in the glorious light of modernism, eclipsing its old darker self which for now remains in shadow, and out of sight. Which is the true face of psychiatry? This is the daunting question put before the audience within the first ten minutes of the film. Ben Kingsley as Cawley is perfectly cast to personify this query. Not for the first time do we see an actor's own history successfully utilised by the actor, director and audience to construct the character and intentions of the psychiatrist in the eyes of the spectator. And here, like his profession, the psychiatrist looks in two directions. He is at once (by day) the softly spoken *Gandhi,* man of peace and rationality, and as well, the possibility (by night) of the repulsive bullying gangster *Don Logan* of *Sexy Beast.*

The two Marshals – Teddy and Chuck – have come to the island to investigate the mysterious disappearance of patient cum prisoner Rachel Solando, a war widow, whose senseless murder of her three children – purposely drowning them in the lake behind her house – led to her detention in the asylum. Hers is a rather different fate to that which awaited the promulgators of other (professional/therapeutic) acts of drowning, referred to above, and deemed by the authorities, despite the numerous fatal outcomes, to constitute legitimate medical interventions. In the account given by Cawley, Rachel has maintained an intricate delusional belief system in which her children are still alive and she is not in an institution. She is said to think she is living in a 'small town in the Berkshires'. She has in fact been in a prison. Cawley thinks it is a hospital! With a glance at the Marshals and a few short words the pipe smoking Cawley promotes Rachel as a circus virtuoso; 'it is as if she evaporated straight through the walls' he suggests, concluding a story of her escape that defies rational explanation. Her cell locked from the outside, the sole window within barred, the island, eleven miles from the nearest landmass, all searched – no trace of her found – a challenge worthy of Harry Houdini. Then there is the puzzle found scribbled on a piece of paper in her cell. There are two lines: 'The law of 4', and below it 'Who is 67?'

Teddy's questioning of those staff that were on duty when Rachel disappeared yields nothing substantial, each reluctant exchange with what resembles an orchestrated ensemble appearing only to service the counterfactual reality generated by Cawley's story. The impossibility of it all ebbs and flows in tandem with the fog through the sound, fashioning a world moving slowly and inexorably outside the fabric of reality – an 'elaborate fictional structure' obscuring the truth. The real and concrete world replaced with a copy perfect in every detail – as with the perfect murder, the perfect crime with the perfect escape (Baudrillard, 1994, 1996). But does the hyper-real isolated world of Ashecliffe Hospital make sense? Rachel is a murderer, but has reality been murdered also?

This fog we will come to realise permeates not just the air of Shutter Island but the narratives of goodness, honour, reason and identity upon which we have built the facade of our cultural history and mythology since World War II. It descends foremost on Teddy Daniels, and weaves its way into the unspoken spaces between the men, and beyond them, to the universe beyond the screen wherein we reside. The mist enveloping all beats time to the reverberating echoes of the *German Trauma* (Sereny, 2001), its unforgiving melody summoning personal and collective remembrance of past horrors. For Teddy, the nihilistic anti-humanity of the concentration camp has been etched into his brain. Intermittently and unpredictably it is resurrected and replayed – images of the typhus epidemic at Dachau, the undignified unfulfilled lives of the frozen dead, and his own frenzied participation in the murder of hundreds of German soldiers there. Photographs of Rachel's drowned children, the music of Mahler, and the quiet condescending demeanour of Cawley's colleague, Dr Jeremiah Naehring, an elderly German, reach into his mind to stir the intoxicating instability of pathos, remorse and hatred. The horrors can never leave Teddy – and though we might like to think otherwise they cling to us too, for on their buried remains have we erected the socio-historical framework of this our culture. There is a difference Teddy says between warfare and murder and he (and we) participated in the latter.

American soldiers did murder German soldiers at the liberated death camp. They murdered countless numbers in Vietnam. The British – inventors of the concentration camp – have also accrued a steady list of war crimes to their name: Dresden, Hamburg, Kenya, Iraq, and no doubt will continue to commit them (Curtis, 2003, 2004).

We never know for certain if Naehring has ties to this recent Nazi past. Is he, as he claims, an innocent refugee or did he, as Teddy believes, belong in the dock at Nuremberg? The US is known to have recruited large numbers of Nazi scientists (these included men who had conducted experiments on inmates at Dachau) under a secret intelligence operation referred to as 'Operation Paperclip' (Lasby, 1975) and was the sole power responsible for conducting the 'Doctors' Trial' at Nuremberg (Whitaker, 2002). A Faustian bargain whereby nefarious scientific and medical skills could be exchanged with the victorious Western powers for freedom was opportune and seems to have been the order of the day. What this likely entailed is that salacious Western doctors learnt from their German colleagues how to plumb new depths in ethical standards of research involving human subjects. Psychiatric patients have always been particularly vulnerable to this because of their status as 'unpeople' (Curtis, 2004).

From Naehring's appearance alone – mild mannered and calm – we can be sure of little – he is as normal as any putative Nazi doctor could be, and so we are left throughout only with circumstantial evidence, tantalising clues that his cold-hearted, even cruel approach marks him out as one with a dubious past. Beyond Dr Naehring evidence of Nazi influence on Shutter Island is strong, with later reference not merely to 'flouting the Nuremberg Code'[1] at Ashecliffe but obliterating it. But as far as Naehring is concerned, his past identity remains relatively unexplored – just as the unsettling participation of the psychiatric profession in the philosophy, preparation, planning and trial run[2] which underpinned the Holocaust remains similarly unexplored by the profession decades later. Read and Masson (2004: 38) remind us that almost all the psychiatrists involved in the Nazi 'mercy' killings 'escaped censure or punishment by the Allies'. 'They all remained silent, denied it and lied, trivialised it in some cases' (Rees, 2005: 76), no doubt because steeped in the medical/psychiatric biological ideology they had been schooled in they were unable to 'arrive at a clear ethical evaluation of what [they] had done and

1. The Nuremberg Code was introduced following the 'Doctors' Trial' of Nazi physicians at Nuremberg. It set out a series of principles for the ethical conduct of research with human participants. These are summarised in the Appendix on page 118.

2. The euthanasia program as it was called involved the state-sanctioned murder of thousands of children with physical impairments as well as so-called 'mental defectives'. It was organised and run by psychiatrists.

what [they] had been part of ' (Lifton, 2000: 8). Morally speaking it could be said the profession remains 'not quite present '(ibid: 8).

Teddy though is carrying much more than the psychological remnants of war. His beloved Dolores, two years deceased, asleep in the cold earth from an arson attack, is no more. His mind cannot fully accommodate this, resurrecting her presence 'like a lit match' (Lehane, 2003: 36) from any trivial circumstance, but none more effective than water. Both fire and water are recurring motifs throughout and suggest not only the workings of Teddy's memory but the primitive alchemy which underpins the psychiatric endeavour. Dolores is most real in Teddy's dreams of magical intensity, still living, feeling and breathing. In a beautiful sequence, Teddy, having fallen asleep pondering the puzzle found in Rachel Solando's cell, finds himself with his wife back in the living room of their home. She is holding an empty bottle of Teddy's, swirling ash like black snow falling around them, the charred air stirred by the slow cascading rhythms of Max Richter's hymn to inevitability 'On the Nature of Daylight'.[3] 'Killed a lot of people in the war,' says Teddy, and in this music, like Mahler's before, is contained the tragedy not just of Teddy's broken life and those trapped in the asylum, but humanity's fallen hopes lost in the ruins of the twentieth century. The talk is cryptic and despairing, syncopated in the saturated language of an evolving nightmare; meanings condensing, degenerating, dissolving, reforming and expanding, each phrase as elusive as the wind. 'She's still here,' says Dolores. 'She never left ... You can't leave.' ... 'She's here you can't leave.' 'Laeddis' (the 'firebug' who 'lit the match that killed her') is here too she tells Teddy. Visually and verbally the dream narrative coalesces into the reality of Teddy's plight, the two worlds woven together are one – their fates entwined. Unlocking the puzzle in either one holds the key to freedom in the other. Dolores implores him; 'You have to let me go ... I'm just bones in a box ... You have to wake up' but Teddy cannot, neither in his imagination nor the real world. Dolores is oozing water from her stomach as he holds her. She is not real, and like the falling snow is turning to ash, disintegrating in burning cinders, crumbling into nothing, reduced like Teddy's hopes to dust. He is alone in a burning house, the water of life seeping through his empty hands, and as he is thrown awake the next morning we are set fair to await the clash of despair, loneliness and imagination with concrete psychiatric power. The dream itself is an affirmation, a declaration of faith in its own creative (Jungian) psychoanalytic power and of the impossibility of reductionist psychiatry to enter the world of human meaning and understand the individual in

3. The title of the piece by German composer Max Richter is particularly apt given the illusory reality which suffuses events unfolding by both day and night.

their own transient symbolic terrain. Beyond this, Teddy's plight is ours, lost in a dream of our own making. 'Sometimes', Freud famously remarked, 'a cigar is only a cigar', but not always. Teddy's dream and his stay at Shutter Island is a metaphor for the world – one that is metaphorically burning – and if we cannot wake up then we too lie at the mercy of the intemperate powers that control it.

Unable to leave the island due to the ferocity of the storm, Teddy and Chuck return to Cawley, seeking permission to interview the patients in Rachel's last group therapy session. They enquire about Rachel's treatment and in an oblique response Cawley returns to the subject of developments in the mental health field. It is 'at war' he says, between the old school, the surgical interventionists whose penchant is for lobotomy[4] – it seems barbaric 'treatments' are not a thing of the past after all – and the new school, the psychopharmacologists who wish to peddle the newly approved drug Thorazine (also known by its generic name chlorpromazine). The year 1954 is held to be the year when the psychopharmacology revolution begins (Moncrieff, 2008), but even at its outset Pierre Deniker and Hans Lehman, both pioneers in the use of Thorazine, compared its effects to that engineered by a frontal lobotomy (cited in Moncrieff, 2008). So the old and new schools referred to by Cawley are not at war after all. They belong to one and the same school – and it is the one we still have today, where drugging people is the treatment of choice and lobotomists are fondly remembered in hagiographies of 'maverick medical geniuses'[5] (El Hai, 2005). Even James Gilligan, the psychiatric consultant for the film, on the surface an enthusiast for the humanistic, psychosocial approach ostensibly supported by Cawley, cannot bring himself to offer an outright condemnation of lobotomy, speaking only of it having been 'overapplied!' In the short feature accompanying the DVD release of the film, Gilligan refrains from telling us just what he therefore considers to be the optimal conditions for hacking into a human being's intact healthy brain. Lobotomy in fact has not completely died away. It remains in use, as one of my own students in recent years sadly testified, having herself been subjected to the practice. Despite so-called refinements in the procedure the effects were noticeable and grave.

Cawley professes he belongs to neither school, and, contemptuous of those who use drugs as a first resort, maintains his belief lies in 'talk therapy' (Lehane, 2003: 119), respecting and listening to his patients. He

---

4. The film dialogue departs slightly here from the text of Dennis Lehane's (2003) novel on which the film is based. In the book (Lehane, 2003: 118–119) Cawley includes shock therapies amongst the activities of the old school.

5. See also Jansson (1998) for a sycophantic defence of Moniz who introduced the procedure and received a Nobel Prize in return. 'There is no doubt that Moniz deserved the Nobel Prize,' says Jansson. Patients would and have disagreed.

positions himself then amongst the declining army of psychoanalysts in the 1950s with an interest in therapeutic dialogue but would that have attracted the interest of intelligence agencies? Most unlikely! And what's more if he is the chief psychiatrist at the facility and with the reputation he has, then surely he would have held more sway over those of his colleagues whose idea of a 'therapeutic alliance' goes no further than a body full of Largactil or a swift slice from a scalpel. Perhaps this apparent contradiction can be resolved if we consider other possibilities. One of course is that he is a hypocrite, like all psychiatrists who use the language of disease in explaining their patients' experiences – his 'moral fusion' in that case is conceptual confusion – 'illnesses' whose natural history can apparently respond to moral exhortation. A more sinister possibility and one which grows in its insistence is that there may be other forces controlling 'medical' developments on the island and Cawley either has little control after all or is fully in agreement with their exercise.

We get further intimations that a German National Socialist sensibility has reached US shores from the Marshals' interviews with the patients, during which, one of them, a 'blond, and pudgy' (Lehane, 2003: 130) man, screams that Rachel Solando should 'be gassed', along with 'retards', 'niggers', and 'killers'. However the replies of many of the patients, like those of the staff, seem stilted and coached. In the course of these interviews Teddy's evident interest in Andrew Laeddis intensifies, and he subsequently tells Chuck that far from this being a routine investigation in the line of his work, he had actually specifically requested the Solando case ('the vanishing lady' as he refers to it) having heard Laeddis had been transferred to the island. He too it seems has vanished. And then there is George Noyce, a convict Teddy has run into in the past who has been a patient in Ashecliffe – in Ward C! Noyce has regaled him with horror stories of drug and lobotomy experiments. Furthermore the hospital has been receiving funds from an unusual source (the House Un-American Activities Committee, HUAC[6]) – for the purpose, Teddy guesses, of 'conducting experiments on the mind'. After all he says, 'Crazy people are the perfect subjects – nobody listens [to them].' Ashecliffe Hospital, a government nursery for unethical research, resembles none other than *The Island of Doctor Moreau,* a monstrous sanctuary of debased experimentation adrift on the seas of reason. And these too are but symbolic renditions of the arts of the 'Master Race' to perfect their ignoble presence on the earth. As Chuck realises, it may be more sinister than they can imagine and paranoia may be the most rational response. 'Everything about this place stinks of government ops,' he says. 'What if they wanted you

---

6. HUAC formed the backbone of the McCarthyist era investigations into communist influence in American life.

here? You were asking questions.' He proposes that Rachel Solando may not even exist! Everything may be a ruse. As it might be for us also, educated as we invariably are to the tune of elite interests.

We are never in fact sure whether Rachel Solando does exist – not even after Cawley abruptly announces she has been found near the lighthouse, nor later when Teddy encounters a woman in the caves below the cliffs claiming that she is the real Rachel Solando, a former psychiatrist on the island. Is she as the '67th patient' the answer to the riddle found in her cell? Teddy's interview with the hospital Rachel yields little beyond the fact that she appears highly disturbed and delusional. She physically attacks Teddy for masquerading as her dead husband. 'Who the fuck are you?' she screams – a question which is to become of paramount importance later. In *Shutter Island* a crisis of truth and identity eventually engulfs everyone. Nobody is who they say they are or think they are.

Teddy's altercation with Rachel leaves him confused, unsteady on his feet, pale and photosensitive as a migraine attacks seizes him. At Cawley's insistence he takes some pills and is propelled into a nightmarish sleep, in which first Laeddis appears smirking, then Chuck, 'clock's ticking my friend, we're running out of time' and finally Rachel, three blood-stained dead children at her feet. 'You should have saved me ...' one of them says, '... you should have saved all of us.' He carries the children to the lake, watching them sink under its tranquil surface and emerges suddenly into wakefulness to find Dolores standing in the mess. Just as in his previous dream, she repeats that Laeddis is 'still here ... you find him and kill him dead.' It is a dream within a dream, though what is real and what is illusion on the island of pain is increasingly opaque. He awakes again to find it is morning, the generator has failed and in the resultant confusion patients have escaped from the facility, giving him an opportunity to investigate the hidden truths of Ward C. Here the dread unconscious of the human world lives and breathes – a veritable house of socially and psychiatrically engineered human wreckage – the stark legacy of eugenic dreams. In the dark and dank cold interior is a pitiful Noyce. 'You're a rat in a maze,' Noyce tells him. 'This isn't about the truth – it's about you.' Again Dolores appears –unshackled for the first time from the bounds of his dreams – but it is now Noyce not Dolores who begs Teddy to let her go. 'If you don't,' he says, 'then you'll never leave this island.' Noyce expresses his own fear that he will be taken to the lighthouse and subjected to experimental brain surgery there. As for Laeddis – there's only one place he can be. And it too is that beacon of darkness, the lighthouse, which once called out to those on the sea.

Teddy must meet his destiny there and, distrustful now of Chuck, is determined to go alone in the fading light. Unable to find a way he returns to the cliff tops and momentarily thinks he spots Chuck's lifeless body below on the rocks. He scrambles down the cliff face. No body is there, but in the back of a fire-lit cave lurks a bedraggled and apparently real Rachel Solando eking out a grim survival. Unmarried and childless she reveals that prior to her incarceration at Ashecliffe she was a doctor there. Like Patrick McGoohan's psychedelic extravaganza on freedom and repression, *The Prisoner*, the 'Kafkaesque genius' of the state's hunger for mind control now dominates proceedings. 'Once you're declared insane, then anything you do is called part of that insanity,' she declares. Of course Rosenhan's (1973) 'experiment' confirmed what we knew – but a generation later, failure to accept a designation of being mentally ill is still considered to demonstrate lack of insight and to constitute a further manifestation that one 'really' is firmly in the grip of a 'mental illness'. Rachel's career as a patient began she tells us when she began questioning the delivery of large quantities of opium-based hallucinogenic drugs and surgical practices – for experimental work designed to 'create ghosts to go out into the world and do ghostly work [to] recreate a man so he doesn't feel pain or love or sympathy, a man who can't be interrogated because he has no memories to confess.' The modern man in short who goes out into the world amnesic to the past, already dead, ready to kill for the state (fight terrorism at home or abroad), tranquilise in its name or else ratchet up the profit margins. Everyone else is fair game for madness.

Teddy has apparently been drugged since his arrival, with due consequences – 'funny dreams, trouble sleeping, headaches' – another involuntary recipient of the 'democratic' response to Cold War fears of North Korean brainwashing, i.e. US brainwashing, the 'learned it from the Nazi's kind' (Lehane, 2003: 310). When the other side engage in these tactics to silence internal troublemakers we call it for what it is, but when we engage in them they become necessary therapy or 'pre-emptive defence'. A philosophy – sometimes called 'realpolitik' that could be mistaken for suggesting 'there is no moral order at all.'[7]

Though invariably a subject of non-discussion in psychological or psychiatric textbooks, the role of behavioural 'science' in remaking and remodelling 'man' – the goal of all totalitarian regimes of the twentieth century – keeps seeping out of the containers of intellectual conformity. *Shutter Island* follows in the footsteps of *The Manchurian Candidate* and the *Bourne* films in exploring this use of coercive psychiatric/psychological 'technology'. That these series of films have appeared in such close proximity to one another in the opening decade[8] of the twenty-first century should be read as an indication of growing concern that the

---

7. A comment of the warden's to Teddy as he makes his way back from the cliffs.

8. *The Manchurian Candidate* was released in 2004, a remake of the original produced in 1962.

powers (psychiatric and intelligence) that wield such technology are moving beyond democratic control and pose a serious threat to the well-being of the population at large. Dennis Lehane, the author of the novel on which the film is based, has indicated that a prime stimulus behind the writing of it was the introduction of the Patriot Act[9] by the Bush administration – 'the greatest assault on our freedoms since McCarthyism' (Lehane, 2010), a signal of the 'mind repression' on the horizon 'if we continue down this road'. As he also makes plain in the preface to the book he was additionally influenced by Robert Whitaker's (2002) history of the mismanagement, outright harm and pseudoscience perpetrated by psychiatrists in the guise of helping the 'mentally ill'. In a chapter entitled 'The Nuremberg Code Doesn't Apply Here', Whitaker reviewed the numerous violations of this code since the war. He noted the failure of mainstream psychiatry, over many decades, to uphold the principle of informed consent when conducting interventions which were experimental in nature, were intended to worsen the state of mind of anyone subjected to them and induced lasting harm.

The meeting with Rachel in the cave and a chance encounter with Cawley means that Teddy has one final climactic fight in front of him. The reality of Teddy Daniel's life as a Marshal on Shutter Island to investigate the disappearance of Rachel Solando is about to evaporate. Another reality will take its place. 'You don't have a partner, you came here alone,' Cawley announces. Teddy must find his way to the lighthouse to uncover the truth. When he does finally reach the barren surreal interior at its summit, we are confronted with a Daliesque set piece. Cawley seated beside a lone desk, telephone and papers to hand, testifies not to the 'persistence of memory' but to its abolition. What he has to say provides not only the solution to the remaining puzzle in Rachel's cell – 'the law of 4' – but points to Teddy's insanity. He is not after all Teddy (Edward) Daniels, that name has been constructed from an anagram of his own – Andrew Laeddis! He is the 67th patient at Ashecliffe, a man, according to his intake papers, who is 'highly intelligent, highly delusional' with a 'known proclivity for violence … the most dangerous patient' on Shutter Island. Rachel Solando is also a figment of his imagination, her name fashioned from the letters of his wife's (Dolores Chanal), and her tragic history, drowning her children by the lake, is none other than Dolores's; and for this Andrew (Teddy) killed her, retreating into a delusional world

---

9. Signed into law in the aftermath of the 9/11 attacks (on October 26th 2001), amongst other things the Act dramatically enhanced law enforcement agencies' ability to search telephone, email, medical, financial, and other records. Title II authorised so-called 'sneak and peak' warrants and roving wiretaps, granting intelligence agencies access to documents that reveal the patterns of US citizens (see http://en.wikipedia.org/wiki USA_PATRIOT_Act).

to protect himself from the pain of what he had done. The events we have witnessed unfold to this point have been a psychodrama scripted by Cawley, as the 'most radical cutting edge role play ever,' in an attempt to pull Andrew back to sanity. Momentarily it seems to awaken memories of his life as Laeddis and the twin traumas of discovering his drowned children and his own consequent murder of his wife. But 'accepting' himself as Andrew Laeddis looks to be short lived. 'Which would be worse,' he finally utters, 'to live as a monster or to die a good man?' His death will be an existential one and the lobotomist's hand will end it.

So, at its conclusion the benevolent image of the psychiatrist is safely restored – a testament to the immense hold the image of the good doctor has on us. The shackling of patients, mind-altering experiments on behalf of the state, importation of Nazi science, torture masquerading as treatment, and prisons as hospitals, are all forgotten, along with the murder of surrendered German soldiers at Dachau. This we are told did not happen. The price of the psychiatrist's power to define reality is the sacrifice of that reality and with it a truer version of history. But there is another possibility to consider during the final scenes of *Shutter Island* – that Teddy is not Andrew Laeddis after all, and that his memories as Laeddis are an experimental creation. Dennis Lehane (2003) has remarked that 'every page [of Shutter Island] is haunted by the spectre of McCarthyism.' Neither he nor we are immune to the rewriting of history. Orwell's Winston Smith had no answer to this, neither do we!

Either interpretation can be made to fit the 'facts', but perhaps the more enduring truth for digestion concerns not one of personal identity but the very real 'evils' of an unethical institutional state-sponsored psychiatry, both historically and contemporaneously. These are not delusions.

Concluding comments
Scorsese's exploration of obsession, intrigue, madness, identity and power owes more than a small debt to Hitchcock, the master of the psychological suspense thriller. In Rachel Solando's disappearance, Teddy Daniels' obsession with Laeddis and the pre-eminence of dream imagery are respective nods to *The Lady Vanishes*, *Vertigo* and *Spellbound* respectively. There are other quintessential Hitchcock motifs: the attention to psychological weakness, an innocent man accused (Teddy), a cool blonde (Teddy's wife Dolores), and characters who switch sides (Chuck). This Hitchcockian style is perfectly suited for a landscape where nothing is as it seems, but in contrast Scorsese's (and Lehane's) subterfuge points to a resolution of the intrigue – not just in the depth of a single character or the relations between characters (though this is employed) – at a much grander political order than anything attempted by Hitchcock. The

voyeur's gaze, we could say, is here pointed at our society. It is this above all else that is not what it seems.

The Anglo-American alliance – the famed 'special relationship' (the 'victors' of World War II – the Russians were until very recently airbrushed out of the picture) – has whitewashed its own history. This is not only with respect to assimilating to its ranks those guilty of horrendous crimes in the last 'great' war, but in presenting itself as the defender of democracy, freedom, and conscience in the days since then, and beyond that as the guardian of the moral principles on which the articles of war were founded. Liu and Hilton (2005) have written how such representations of a nation's past come to play a key role in shaping the identities of its citizens, and whilst they also note that the 'management and negotiation' of these are 'central to interethnic and international relations' (Liu & Hilton, 2005: 537) it could be added here that they are also critical of how a people (or at least the elite powers who govern them) define standards of sanity and madness. Social representations however should not be taken as flags of truth and any cursory examination of the actual historical record will suffice to confirm this (Chomsky, 2010).

Western psychiatry, now a functioning arm of government in the social control of the 'masses', is subject to these same 'laws' of representation, its treatment of its own aims and history censored and distorted beyond recognition. Allied with elite power, psychiatry long ago declared its own war on the rebellious, the distressed, the nonconforming, the just plain different and of necessity the truth. The recruitment of Nazi scientists under Operation Paperclip spawned several more – 'Project Bluebird (renamed Artichoke)' amongst them which specialised in mind-control, interrogation, and behaviour modification techniques, which in turn led to the CIA-sponsored MKULTRA, and the infamous experiments in brainwashing and mind control conducted by Ewen Cameron in the 1950s (Harper, 2007) whose consequences are still reverberating with us today. Psychiatry has persistently shied away from acknowledging this murky history – all well documented. The uncomfortable facts it has shut out. *Shutter Island* asks, not merely what is real in the Asylum of 1954, but what is real about the past we have been so thoroughly schooled to believe in. Insomuch as we are concerned with the shifting sands on which the edifice of our benevolent self-image has been erected, we must seek to know who the gatekeepers and guardians of past truths are. Any scrutiny of the critical literature will tell us that we cannot look to the behavioural sciences in general, or psychiatry in particular, to assist us in this task. Consequently, as pre-Cold War memories enjoy a global thaw, the renascent horrors flowing into the present belong not solely to Teddy Daniels. To the extent that we believe in the past that we do, we are all in some way implicated in the denial and fabrication of history.

Connerton (2009) has argued how the erasure of the past is implicit in the changes wrought by modernity – changes in physical geography, consumerism and social relationships, but what we are talking about here is a thing apart from accidental forgetting. Ours is intentional. We have remembered only the victory of the battle with Nazism – 'the good war' (Curtis, 1995), not the defeat that came with it. The German trauma is also ours. From our close proximity to it we learnt about the exercise of power and the deceitful arts of memory. In all cultures which have either perpetrated or been complicit in mass murder and not been held accountable for it there is a collective amnesia. Ours is no different – psychiatry polices this amnesia in ours. This policing function arguably accelerated in the period depicted in *Shutter Island*. Such 'historical amnesia' carries great dangers, beyond its capacity to undermine 'moral and intellectual integrity'; it also, as (Chomsky, 2010: 268) rightly observed, sows the seeds for future crimes. It is not hard to imagine why the 1950s were ripe for the 'orgy of experimentation' (Moncrieff, 2008: 32) that spanned the decade. Following the confrontation with fascism and the aftershocks of the Great Depression, overt violence and economic subjugation were no longer viable or indeed palatable means of controlling populations. What better way to control people than from the inside? In this light, the expansion of psychiatry through the medicalisation of everyday life (Szasz, 2007b) can be seen as a continuation of this project with the same unwilling subjects.

Shutter Island is an unusual film in many ways – not least in the manner in which it brings a dystopian lens to the past rather than the future. Along with science fiction works such as *Blade Runner* it deals with the manipulation of memory and the uncertainties of identity in a bleak emotional and political landscape. Teddy Daniels, like Rutger Hauer's replicant in Ridley Scott's film, has also 'done terrible things' and 'seen things you wouldn't believe', and many people having seen the film will still not believe them either, locating the real world in Teddy Daniels' insanity. As the 'real' Rachel Solando says to Teddy, 'If you're not crazy but people have told the world you are, then all your protests to the contrary just underscore their point.' Thus the world revealed in Ashecliffe Hospital is more disturbing than the celluloid translation of Philip K. Dick's novel, because it questions the veracity not of the (fictional) world as seen through one of the characters, however symbolic it is of ours – but of our own, the one we hold to be true.

The subject matter of tampering with memory concerns not just the residents of Shutter Island but the inhabitants of the Western democracies (and the denizens of non-democratic states too). It raises for consideration the radical possibility that the world we have believed in for so long – a free and benevolent society with righteous armed forces, caring doctors and psychiatrists working for our benefit – is itself a work of fiction, one authored to maintain 'the existing structure of socioeconomic privilege' (Chomsky, 2010: 67). Ergo, can our memories, let alone Teddy Daniels' be trusted? *Shutter Island* posits more drastically than any science fiction film could the disappearance of the world – the one we take to be real. It has in effect 'murdered reality' (Baudrillard, 1996). But this is a necessary crime if we are to wake up and discover it anew. It is not just that something is amiss in the state of Denmark, it is exponentially more serious. We have been misled by modernity. Hiding away in a cave, with no hope of escape from the island Rachel Solando remarks, 'A half century from now, people in the know will look back and say this ... this is where it all began ...' Tellingly, in her observation that psychiatry has successfully deluded 'most of society for over half a century' Moncrieff (2008: 13) subscribes to the same timeline. Hitler's surviving secretary Traudl Junge, when interviewed by Gitta Sereny, felt that at the end of it all Hitler had left the German people with 'a nothing (*ein Nichts*)' (Sereny, 2000: 362). In the sum total of useful knowledge this is what psychiatry has left us. We are in 'the zero hour' (Curtis, 1995). After *Shutter Island* 'ein Nichts' is at least somewhere to start.

Chapter Two

Changeling: Law, liberty and psychiatry

We rely on our good friends in the police department to point to us those people who exhibit behaviour which is socially unacceptable.

Dr Steele

Clint Eastwood's *Changeling* is the first in a trilogy of films to be considered in this volume which dramatise the lives of real people who through force of circumstance found themselves entangled in the net of the psychiatric system. The film tells the story of Christine Collins (played by Angelina Jolie), a working-class telegraphic supervisor in 1920s Los Angeles whose ride on the wheel of unfortunate fate began following the kidnap and murder of her son Walter. As the events portrayed in the film occurred over eight decades ago, inevitable and legitimate questions about the historical accuracy of the portrayal can be raised. In response to such concerns screenwriter Michael J. Straczynski has described how he constructed much of the script verbatim from several thousand pages of historical documents, court transcripts, and public speeches drawn from the archives of Los Angeles City Hall shortly before they were due to be incinerated. His screenplay adhered closely to this public record, necessarily so in his view. With what was already a bizarre story, he felt that to tamper with it too much would not only undermine its integrity but also detract from its disturbing power.

Given the generally accepted fidelity of the screenplay and film to the historical record – the tale of Christine Collins raises important questions about how the behaviour of the psychiatric authorities and their role in the affair is remembered – if at all. Prior to Straczynski and Eastwood's resurrection of the story it would be fair to say that despite its extraordinary nature[1] it no longer resided within the zone of public recollection. Works such as this which return to the past and reawaken interest in a specific period, place and events play a significant role in the manufacture of social memory and the lay reconstruction of the past. Since of the continuity of human actions link the organisational, social and interpersonal transformations of the past to the present, how we remember the past

---

1. It concerns one of the largest mass killings in Los Angeles' colourful criminal history.

influences how we see the present and what we expect of the future. One of the key themes explored in this and other chapters relates to the presentation of psychiatric history – principally what has been preserved, edited, added or deleted and how this representation impacts on our contemporary trust in the institution. Whilst other chapters will examine particular aspects of this history – of major concern in this one will be psychiatry's relationship to the legal organs of the state. To pursue this analysis we must return to the tale of Christine Collins and her missing son.

In the thick of the Great Depression, on the 10th March 1928, Walter Collins, nine years old, vanished from in front of his family home. A subsequent nationwide search yielded nothing until five months after his disappearance police announced Walter had been found. The exact circumstances which propelled Arthur Hutchens, Jr. to claim to be the missing Collins boy are not fully explored in the film. James Jeffrey Paul's (2008) account of the Wineville murders – as the abductions and brutal slayings of Walter Collins and upwards of 20 other young boys came to be known – provides further details of how and why Hutchens adopted the role of Christine Collins' son. Cecilia Rasmussen (1999) writing in the *Los Angeles Times* also provides a tidy synopsis of the saga. These accounts rely heavily on the press reports of the day which, owing to the interest generated by the film, are available online courtesy of *Los Angeles Times* journalist Larry Harnisch.[2] Police were initially contacted about a possible sighting of Walter by an Illinois diner, and Hutchens, apparently en route to Southern California and an imagined future in the Hollywood dream factory where he hoped to meet his hero Tom Mix, seized on the interest shown him by Christine Collins and the Los Angeles Police Department (LAPD) in order to reach the geographical first leg of his destination. But Hollywood fantasies were not the only motivating force in the runaway boy's life – he was fleeing a dysfunctional family – unhappy with his malicious stepmother and a father with a history of sexual offences against boys. Notwithstanding the omission of these details in the movie – once he was in LA, at a train station reunion organised by the publicity hungry police force, Collins immediately saw that Hutchens was not her son. Not only was he several inches shorter than Walter, but once back at the Collins home he was also discovered, unlike the real Walter, to have been circumcised. Other physical discrepancies also emerged. That Hutchens even made it to the Collins home at all once Mrs Collins had expressed her opinion, is largely because of the insistence of the police captain in charge of the case – J.J. Jones – that she 'try him out for a couple of weeks'.[3] The trial adoption spearheaded by Jones in the manner of road

2. See http://latimesblogs.latimes.com/thedailymirror/changeling/
3. This exchange is described in City Council hearing transcripts of the day … contd

testing a consumer product duly failed. After three weeks had elapsed
Collins had had enough of the impostor and returned him, vehemently
insisting that this was not her son.

Initially a missing person's investigation, the Collins case had become
a vehicle for rejuvenating the declining public image of the police, the
return of the boy nothing more than a photo opportunity – a way of
burying bad news we might say today. Against this, there was oral and
written evidence from Walter's teaching staff and dentist. Though this
provided overwhelming support for the view that the boy placed in Mrs
Collins' charge by the LAPD was not her son, it counted for little. The
LAPD's thirst for positive column inches and fear of the truth saw it turn
to the medical and psychiatric establishment to bolster its flimsy position.
As with the death of Ian Tomlinson following the intervention of the
Metropolitan Police during the G20 protests of April 2009, members of this
establishment were ready and willing to collude. Eastwood has us privy
to the mistreatment of Mrs Collins by LAPD medical lackey and so-called
'child specialist', Earl W. Tarr. His pseudoscientific theories to explain the
physical and behavioural discrepancies between her real son and the
LAPD-supported substitute[4] provide an instructive example of how
'perfectly sound medical explanation[s]' may be nothing of the sort. This
is a brief but telling warning about the power of scientific language in the
wrong hands and in the wrong place. It is also instructive as to why
people who lack scientific education may also singularly lack faith in what
they are being told. The working-class educated Collins knew what she
knew – that the boy was not hers – and refused to discount the value of
her experience in the face of a bullying and tyrannical police force which
sought to discredit her. As the child's mother, challenging their authority
she was declared to be blinded by 'intuition and emotion' and 'was in no
position to be objective!' State legislated reason was mandated to prevail.

With this rejection and her public affirmation of it Collins at once
invoked the ire of the LAPD. Already under mounting public pressure
from a series of corruption scandals and now acutely embarrassed by their
public failure to find the real Walter Collins, they sought to silence and
remove the source of their frustration. As a department 'ruled by violence,
abuse, murder, corruption and intimidation' and intolerant of 'dissent,
contradiction or embarrassment' this was nothing new. Captain Jones
accuses her of 'shirking her responsibility as a mother', insists that she has
been 'trying to … make a lot of fools out of us … and have the state
provide' for her son. Her stoic refusal to sanction police incompetence

---

contd … unearthed by the screenwriter (Changeling Production Notes, accessed September,
2010). The dialogue in the film sees Jones implore Mrs Collins to take him home for two
weeks on a trial basis.

4. These ranged from submerged memory to the deleterious effects of trauma on height.

means that she has 'no business walking the streets of Los Angeles'. The deadly stratagem of thwarted power is then brought into play. If Collins insists on the truth then she is either 'lying' or incapable of knowing if she's 'lying or telling the truth'. To Jones she must therefore be 'a derelict mother' or 'nuts'.

For failing to accord with the police version of events, Collins is found guilty of 'thought crime' and psychiatrically framed; 'defendant states she has been deceived by police and others, and that they have given her a boy and tried to make her think it is her son when she says it is not ... she suffers from paranoia and delusions of persecution and dislocation from reality. She may be a threat to herself or others.' Collins, as we know, was being deceived by police, who did try to foist another child onto her as her own; she was therefore a 'threat' to them and 'dislocated' from their reality – all of which testifies to her sanity. However the nature of psychiatric language – and the insidious power of the conquered nouns and verbs ('reality', 'deceive', 'dislocation', 'treatment') within its lexicon – suggest that once anyone has been subject to its linguistic armoury they will appear to any naive outsider to be incapable of reason and good sense. The means to achieving the police objectives is thus the removal of Collins to psychiatric facilities – the 'psychopathic ward', so called, of the Los Angeles County Hospital. This according to Jones, displaying an impressive fluency with psychiatric linguistics, constitutes 'protective custody', her disagreement with him is a 'mental breakdown' and what she is to receive at the hospital is apparently, 'the best treatment available'. Little did the police realise however that the dragons of publicity they had so carelessly unleashed would return to consume them, but not before Christine Collins had endured five days of 'hospitality' in psychiatric captivity.

Collins was incarcerated under a 'Code 12' statute which allowed for the internment, without warrant or due legal process of any person considered difficult or inconvenient. The subjects of these orders were frequently women – sex workers, aggrieved wives, vagrants and – as in Collins' case – those who had found themselves in direct dispute with the police. Something was judged to be 'wrong' with Collins precisely because she acted resolutely and firmly – and this was 'alien' to the patriarchal systems governing psychiatry and law enforcement. Such 'crass violation[s] of contemporary concepts of fundamental human rights' (Szasz, 1983: 113) are difficult to find in modern societies outside the field of psychiatry – with the possible exception of current anti-terror legislation through which people can be jailed for their unwanted opinions or choice of reading material.[5] The common thread linking

5. See for example Jenkins (2009).

psychiatry to 'terrorism' is that the state believes it should have the right to deprive people of liberty if they hold particular views which state elites decree constitute a 'danger' to their normal modes of functioning. Furthermore to hold such views at all is considered a priori to be indicative of aberrant mental functioning. As Szasz (1983: 120) suggests, the incursion of psychiatric thinking into political discourse has by now become so routine that the list of the accused has become virtually 'endless'. As such, the linguistic-psychiatric abuse – by means of attributions of mental instability – of those who challenge or upset power at any level, be it in any organisation, is now so thoroughly ingrained in the mindset of the powerful that it gives all the appearance of being a reflex action.

The depiction of Christine Collins' short detention in the LA psychiatric residence offers a condensed guide to the brutalities and Kafkaesque logic which characterise and have always characterised the operation of psychiatry as a pseudomedical scientific enterprise acting on behalf of the state. It is an enterprise with a penchant for strong-arm tactics. On her admission any attempt to utilise reason to explain her predicament is met with threats to wrap her in a straightjacket. The rules of psychiatry operate such that any attempt to implicate centres of social power (e.g. the police, the medical profession, political and other organisations) in acts of deliberate harm, wrongdoing or deception, which it is against the interests of those organisations to admit to, runs the risk of being attributed to a (fictitious) biomedical disorder. This is all the more likely when the acts engaged in by those powers are said to have been carried out covertly, which given their unsavoury nature is more than likely to be the case. If the attributions made are not of outright insanity then the person out of favour can always be labelled a conspiracy theorist – a resident in the halfway house to madness. In the absence of independent corroborating evidence any claims of insanity or diagnoses of mental illness occurring in such a scenario are unfalsifiable. As psychiatric diagnoses and attributions of sanity/insanity customarily lack such evidence it is apparent that such practices belong firmly in the realm of politics not science. Psychiatry should logically therefore be considered a form of political rather than scientific practice and one which is no less afraid than others in its stable to sanction the use of dirty tricks.

Collins's initiation into the LA County Hospital Psychopathic Ward begins with her physical degradation, forced to stand naked, hosed down with a shower and subject to an intimate physical examination, a rite of passage in which control over her own body has been (forcibly) relinquished – a sign that for the duration of her internment it is in the possession of the custodians of psychiatric 'care'. Once this physical ordeal is over she is shown to a dilapidated cell and informed that the zone of control extends beyond her body to sources of information from the outside world. Newspapers, magazines, radios and books are now imbued with the status of forbidden objects. All this supposedly is for her 'own good'. She is being returned to a state in which she is permitted to exercise the physical autonomy and agency expected of an infant. This is what the hospital demands – it is a de facto region of totalitarian control. Collins' human initiation into life in the hospital is provided by another patient, Carol Dexter in a breakfast room, chock-full of vacant lobotomised and electro-shocked female patients. Dexter instructs her on the politics of appearing normal. Collins' 'Code 12' referral has brought her into the depths of a catch-22. Dexter explains:

> *The more you try to act sane, the crazier you start to look. If you smile too much, you're delusional or stifling hysteria. If you don't smile, you're depressed. If you're neutral you're emotionally withdrawn and potentially catatonic.*

It's a no-win situation, one which Rachel Solando enunciated in *Shutter Island*. Everything in a patient's behavioural repertoire is now construed as a manifestation of mental illness. While critics of the psychiatric profession, both professional and lay (see for example Read & Reynolds, 1996) have repeatedly laid bare this fundamental problem with psychiatric diagnosis and practice, the profession carries on regardless, as if blissfully unaware, steadfastly refusing to acknowledge or address it. Reason is no defence against it. It can only be answered with power. Dexter has been sectioned as a consequence of her night work in the sex trade and is savvy to the interlocking roles which the police and mental health system play in the subjugation of women. They are to be given a Pavlovian lesson in acquiescence. Learn to 'shut up' or kiss goodbye to a free life outside the institution. The only way out for dissenting women comes with the price of a lobotomy.

Shortly after her encounter with Carol Dexter, Collins gets to meet her medical overlord, the aptly named Dr Jonathan Steele.[6] Steele is ruthless, officious, cold, and menacing, determined only to catch Collins out and exhibit his power. She is not wise to the unplayable nature of the game she has entered and tries vainly to tell him what she thinks he would need to hear in order to be convinced of her sanity. That though is not his purpose. He is seeking only to demonstrate that she has 'trouble telling fantasy from reality'. His gambit is premised on the notion that the 'police are here to protect us'. If Collins denies this, she is found 'guilty' of paranoid

---

6. Newspaper reports of the time actually list the attending physician variously as 'M.D. Steele' or 'E.E. Steele', an apt name for one in control of a totalitarian organisation.

ideation. If she affirms it, she must deny the reality of her predicament. A subsequent refusal to take medication for compulsory relaxation earns her a further rebuke and an unscheduled appointment with the good doctor. 'There's nothing wrong with me that I need medication,' she cries, to which Steele's response is that she should prove this by signing an affidavit certifying that the boy brought to her by the police is her son, that they were right to send her to the hospital and that she absolves them of all responsibility. With courage she declines, a blow to the police-psychiatric confederacy. Steele translates this resistance into psychiatric speak – her 'condition has not improved', and her consequent anger at this outrage are signs of her becoming 'agitated' and 'hysterical' which must be dealt with by forced 'medication' – the time-honoured euphemism for drug-induced silencing. In any other setting than an ostensibly medical one this would be interpreted unambiguously as assault.

Given our first glimpse of what is a familiar refrain in the study of cinematic psychiatry – not to say the lives of patients down the years – the use of 'treatment' as punishment, we are quickly given our second. As Dexter tries to intervene to prevent Collins being drugged she is hit by Steele, provoking a retaliatory strike by the woman. On Steele's orders Dexter is then dragged off screaming to 'Room 18', pinned down and strapped to a trolley by five members of staff and administered ECT. Unintentionally or not, the 'Code 12s' and 'Room 18s' of this world can be read as a damning indictment of institutional (psychiatric) care by numbers. It was a warning that contrived organisational (legal and scientific) responses to the complexity of human problems that reduce action and people to a series of categories and codes are not only intrinsically wrong, and affronts to human dignity but also intrinsically violent. They are as equally inappropriate to resolving human misery as Eastwood's *Dirty Harry* and his famed .44 Magnum were to solving crime.

Collins herself looks set for shock treatment. As with Carol Dexter, this was to be no scientifically based procedure to alleviate suffering but a penalty designed to teach her a lesson for her 'obstinate' refusal to take needless sedating drugs or kowtow to the authority of the police-psychiatric alliance. Eastwood portrays Collins' release from hospital and her eleventh hour reprieve from ECT as the outcome of Gustav Briegleb's robust intervention, brandishing a *Los Angeles Times* article naming Walter as a possible victim in the Wineville killings. In this scenario, Eastwood has undoubtedly employed a degree of cinematic licence. Whilst Briegleb most certainly championed Collins and supported her subsequent lawsuit against the LAPD, in actuality Collins' release owed more to the fact that Hutchens had, in an interview with Captain Jones, owned up to the hoax.[7]

---

7. *Los Angeles Times*, September 21st, 1928.

Whilst the cinematic depiction and the contemporary journalistic reports of these events differ, the logic in their divergent propositions is much the same. In the face of adverse publicity attendant upon the exposure of Hutchens' real identity and the impending revelations a propos the Wineville murders, the police/medical authorities knew the game was up. It was no longer possible to credibly defend their stance on the boy. Accordingly they had to bow to a greater power –the might of public opinion aided on this occasion by something approaching an independent press. At the time, as Collins was released, Dr Steele told reporters that she had never exhibited any unusual behaviour during the period of her 'observation'. Welcome as Collins' freedom no doubt was – this admission from Steele hardly reflects well on his profession. The important issue is why he and the system in which he worked was content to accept a woman admitted against her will despite having committed no crime and exhibiting no aberrant or dangerous behaviour whatsoever. The simple answer to this is that psychiatrists as agents of social control see such violations of people's human rights as perfectly routine. Many things may have changed in psychiatry in the intervening years, but this is not one of them.

Once again a free woman, Mrs Collins sought a grand jury investigation of her imprisonment and successfully sued Captain Jones for her forced hospitalisation for the sum of $10,800. Earlier accused of being blinded by 'intuition and emotion', the police defence for her imprisonment moved to asserting that she had acted 'strangely … cool, aloof and *unemotional'*. It was not her behaviour which was 'disturbing' as claimed by the police – but theirs for submitting her, for political reasons, to incarceration and the psychiatric system for accepting her – also for political (non-medical) reasons. Collins won her case, though Jones never paid her a cent, despite repeated attempts over the years to get him to do so. Although both he and the Chief of Police James E. Davis were removed from their posts, what the film does not make clear is that both were later reinstated and LA police corruption continued. The reality of entrenched power and its stubborn resistance to attack is presumably not the message that the filmmakers wished the audience to take home with them from the auditorium. Collins' true lasting victory however lay in the legal realm. While mental health system abuses would continue, the extrajudicial system of captivity operated by the LAPD came to an end; they would no longer be able to commit anyone without the due legal process of a warrant. For many people, women in particular, this made a difference.

During her entanglement with the LAPD and their psychiatrist friends Collins repeatedly implored the authorities to continue the search for her son. Whilst centred on Collins' fight for justice the film also explores the nature of her son's fate, kidnapped, sexually abused, tortured and murdered by Gordon Stewart Northcott, and Collins' relationship with Northcott following his arrest and trial. That the tale is an unusual one is, to say the least, something of an understatement. The film, well received at its initial presentation at the Cannes Film Festival, failed by two votes to win the coveted *Palme d'Or*, its loss attributed by the screenwriter to the fact that some of the judges found it hard to believe that the police would have treated Collins as they did (Davis, 2008). In response to this Straczynski annotated the screenplay with his source material. That Northcott was arrested, tried and convicted at all was largely due to the testimony of his nephew Sanford Clark and the forensic evidence of human remains subsequently recovered from the ranch. Clark, held prisoner on Northcott's chicken ranch, was subjected to constant physical and sexual violence, made to participate in several of the murders committed by Northcott and forced to cover up evidence of the deeds by burning and burying the bodies (Paul, 2008; Flacco & Clark, 2009). At least twenty children are believed to have been slain there by Northcott. Clark identified Walter Collins from police photographs as one of Northcott's victims. An inevitable question is whether prompt police action unattended by psychiatric complicity in inaction would have led to a different fate for Walter and any of the other children. Most likely the answer is not. However it is undeniable that the corrupt, bungling investigation of Walter's case and the support lent to it by the Los Angeles mental health system did nobody any favours and a good many people considerable harm. Even after Clark's testimony and Northcott's conviction[8] and execution, Christine Collins continued to believe in the possibility that her son might still be alive. No doubt this is an understandable response on the part of a grieving mother clinging to the last vestiges of hope for her son. One component, however, in this refusal to accept where the evidence pointed is that by this stage and with good reason, any trust she may have once placed in the actions and declarations of authority had been eroded. The psychiatric presence in the film ends with the release of Collins.

No attempt is made to explore the questions about Northcott's sanity, which were raised at the time of his trial and perhaps this was deliberately so in a film which unequivocally argues in favour of the strength of agency and accountability. One of Northcott's legal team had sought to invoke the insanity plea, citing the views of several defence psychiatrists who considered him to be suffering from 'defective glandular activity', 'dementia praecox', and 'extreme abnormal sexual activity' all of which were held to be due to a 'congenital degeneracy' operative 'at the time of

---

8. Though absent from the film, Northcott's mother, Sarah Louise was tried and convicted for Walter's murder. It is unclear to what extent her confession was an attempt to protect her son from the gallows.

the alleged commission of the crime' (Paul, 2008: 143). Some of the prominent psychiatric reasoning of the day to 'explain' Northcott's mental state also resorted to phrenological analysis. The defendant's 'unusually long' chin, 'musical' ears, 'primitive' nose and 'small amount of head back of ears' were deemed sufficient to explain his 'crafty', 'cold', 'sinister' and 'destructive' (ibid: 120) psychological make-up. With the supposed benefits of hindsight this analysis may strike us as absurd. However there are legitimate questions as to whether the attributions of 'dementia praecox' (what is now called schizophrenia) or 'congenital degeneracy' were built on scientific foundations any firmer than diagnoses arrived at from the shape of one's skull. Many would consider the answer to this lies in the negative.

Two psychiatrists withdrew from the defence team, unable to support the insanity plea (Kendrick, 1929). The presiding judge (George R. Freeman) sensibly denied the defence counsel's motion, taking the view that the desire to change Northcott's plea was arrived at as a matter of expediency. Can diagnosis after the fact, in the absence of independent corroborating material evidence of prior 'illness' (see also Chapter 5) ever be anything other than expediency? On the basis of independent evidence, Northcott was adjudged by Freeman to be fully capable of reason; he enjoyed the capacity to distinguish right from wrong, and knew the likely consequences of his actions. He was not therefore to be 'relieved from the responsibility of [his] crimes' (ibid: 224). Prior to his trial Northcott had already made plain his intention to 'play crazy' (ibid: 124). His attempted use of the insanity defence (it did not end in court) was an absurdity – the reasoned resort to a course of action which attempted to demonstrate the absence of reason. As Christine Collins iterates in an exchange with her son, 'for some people responsibility is the scariest thing in the world'. In our present age, this fear grows by the day, feeding an insatiable mental health system. In the mental health game responsibility is now a commodity to be auctioned, bartered and exchanged at the drop of a hat. No price can be put on that folly.

While behind bars in San Quentin, Northcott saw Mrs Collins on several occasions, even on one occasion proposing a face-to-face meeting so that she could be told the truth about her son. The meetings between them, strange as they may seem, are not a Hollywood fiction; prison authorities relaxed their own rules in order to permit them to go ahead. Mrs Collins sought closure and the possibility of resuming her life. Any hopes that the meetings would be useful however came to nought. Throughout the investigation of the murders Northcott had successively toyed with police, alternately confessing and retracting claims. He would swing between blaming his nephew Sanford and his parents and in turn offer to reveal where his victims' bodies had been buried, only to later deny all knowledge of any crimes committed. He was a highly disturbing young man (aged 22 at the time he committed the murders and almost 24 at the time of his execution), a predator upon children and addicted to the attention of others. The lure of Christine Collins to his cell one last time was merely another manipulative ploy, with information about her son dangled as bait. Throughout the entire affair she had been enmeshed in a web of organisational and individual duplicity.

Concluding comments

Changeling is considered to be a critical examination of several interlocking subjects – the disempowerment of women, corruption in political hierarchies and the use of violence against children.[9] Although these issues undoubtedly take up a considerable portion of the two and one quarter hours of screen time, the film should be seen as occupying a more extensive thematic canopy than this. At its centre is a dissertation on the twin antagonists of truth and falsehood.

The title[10] centres on the role of the young impostor, Arthur Hutchens but Hutchens Jnr. is far from being the only fake swaggering through the streets of Southern California. When Gustav Briegleb (John Malkovich), a local Presbyterian minister and pioneer radio evangelist is heard lambasting Los Angeles as 'a place where our protectors have become our brutalizers', his words, aimed as they are at the corrupt hierarchy that run the police force, could just as well point to those with a licence to practise medicine, who, beneath a psychiatric cloak, used their power to intimidate, silence, threaten, and blackmail their 'patients' into behavioural submission.

The Collins case as exemplified in *Changeling* and in particular Briegleb's invective against the LAPD raise more challenging questions than may at first seem apparent. The everyday successful functioning of any society depends crucially on the trust which citizens place in the organs and institutions of their society. This trust sets limits on the political legitimacy of a society and in a healthy functioning democracy is something usually taken for granted. However its breakdown is a recurring motif in the catalogue of societies in which the state has terrorised the population and unleashed mass violence on its inhabitants (Kaldor, 2001). Customarily, whatever misgivings exist about the motives of our political masters, an underlying assumption of their (and our) essentially benign nature prevails (Roberts, 2007). *Changeling* not only demonstrates that our trust in political authority may be misplaced and these assumptions open to challenge, it also posits psychiatry, adorned

---

9. See the Wikipedia discussion http://en.wikipedia.org/wiki/Changeling_(film)
10. In European myth a changeling is a child substituted by fairies for the parents' true child.

with its pivotal role in the sanctioning of admissible behaviour, to be a dangerous bedfellow when allied to its Big Brother partners in power.

This terrain, the mapping of the boundaries of legitimate and illegitimate power, was one which Stanley Milgram's (1974) experiments famously explored to such notable effect. What is particularly noteworthy about psychiatry is that it functions Janus-faced on these borders – one side looking in the direction of Hippocrates and the other toward hypocrisy. Its *raison d'être* is not so much to heal the wounded as to detect abnormality, and by detecting it justify and strengthen its own jurisdiction over the masses. Its continued expansion in the face of scandal after scandal testifies to its relentless drive for power. Accordingly psychiatry reinforces and upholds the prevailing standards of normality and what corresponds to the status quo. Putting to one side the question of whether there should be any 'medical' standards of normality at all when it comes to human conduct – an issue for ethics and politics, not science – the fundamental problem with this is that throughout human history the status quo has always embodied one or other branch of tyranny. This is why Szasz's writings have been replete with comparisons of psychiatry to the Inquisition, witch-finders and slaveholders. Psychiatrists by and large not only fail to get the point, but by virtue of their necessary retreat from historical analysis and embrace of scientism are destined never to get it. There can be no reflexivity if one's colours are nailed to the mast of conformity. Christine Collins is locked up not just because she threatens the public image of the LAPD, but also because she is a woman fighting on behalf of her child, and in 1920s America women and children are judged to have fewer rights than men. That was the status quo and that is what psychiatry seeks to maintain.

The clash between public lies and private truths operates throughout the movie as indeed it was played out in real life – evident not only in the lies perpetrated by the LAPD and the medical psychiatric establishment, but also by Arthur Hutchens and Gordon Stewart Northcott. This is a further reason why audiences find the story so disturbing. While Eastwood was criticised for the conventional and unsensationalised treatment of the story,[11] this facet of the narrative can actually be seen as lending an important counterweight to the protean forces within it working to obscure the truth. In Jolie's character, Christine Collins, this clash is of immense significance, arguably even more so for contemporary viewers. An unholy alliance between international media conglomerates and political governance, allied to the technologies of behavioural control, raise the dangers of organised misrepresentation by an order of some magnitude. The very possibility of this clash is what the totalitarian

11. See http://en.wikipedia.org/wiki/Changeling_(film)

society seeks to eliminate by its abolition of the public–private distinction. All truths will be in the public domain. Briegleb tells Collins that 'most people believe what they hear from the police or the government'. Though no longer straightforwardly true, the message alludes to a truth that still resonates in our age. The everyday social reality endorsed by millions remains the product of a self-proclaimed elite authority which for some time has been taking us down a dangerous path. It is imperative therefore that we take steps to safeguard a future in which there is still choice as to what we think and what we believe. This cannot be taken for granted.

In the production notes, Eastwood stresses the importance of 'plant[ing] your feet and tell[ing] the truth' even when pressured to do otherwise. These sentiments illustrate both the strength and limitations of *Changeling*. In giving us Christine Collins' story, and eschewing a sensationalist approach to the Wineville murders, one which other directors may have been tempted to adopt, the film honours the awful truth of what transpired. However, shining a light on just one corner of psychiatry's murky past increases the probability that its present-day operatives will avoid scrutiny and emerge critically unscathed. A discipline which employs, amongst other tactics, the ever-present 'rhetoric of benevolence' (Cohen, 1985: 20) in its quest to abolish its past can only truly be held to account when the legacy of that past can be seen in the present. Only then can the ever-present 'reality' of miracle cures and imminent research breakthroughs, premised on the continual mistreatment of human beings, be deconstructed to its corporate and state-backed sponsors. It would be unfair to have expected Eastwood's film – a story rooted in one time and one place – to have attempted the same feat. While *Shutter Island*, which explicitly sought such linkage, therefore functions as a more appropriate vehicle for deconstruction, it is sufficient for now that *Changeling* has exposed the interlocking visions of social control which tie the mental health and justice systems together.

Chapter Three

Donnie Darko: Something wicked this way comes

I think I only have a few days left … before they catch me.

Donnie Darko (In Kelly, 2003: 87)

It's 1988; Democratic Presidential candidate, Michael Dukakis is heading for electoral failure and political oblivion. Rumoured to have undergone psychiatric treatment at some unspecified point in his past, he is roundly defeated by George Bush I. This paves the way some years later for the White House resurrection of the family dynasty in the guise of his progeny and former problem drinker George W., who was able and willing to seize power and precipitate global instability by means of illegal war in Iraq. Sixteen years old, Donnie Darko is heading for psychological and existential oblivion in a world reverberating with symbolic richness. Sullen, vacant and morose, at odds with his Republican family, facial features in the icy grip of the Antarctic stare,[1] he is undergoing psychiatric treatment for 'paranoid schizophrenia' under the watchful eye of wistful, and perplexed, but always humane psychiatrist Dr Lilian Thurman (played by Katharine Ross, of *The Graduate* fame). Donnie is faced with global instability of a very different kind. This attempt to save his mind – he is presumably considered a danger to himself or others – necessitates a course of mind-altering pills coupled with psychotherapeutic sessions on the couch, the best client-centred psychotherapy money can buy – with a dash of hypnosis added for good measure. 'Only in America' can one be listened to with such empathic intent while having one's brain stewed by mind-altering chemicals. The question of whether Donnie has chosen of his own free will to be administered this cocktail of interventions is left unexplored, although given his status as a minor and his manifest general attitude toward authority he has most likely been psychiatrised under duress – one of millions. He can be thankful however that he is not encountering the mental health system in earlier times when his estrangement from those with power might have seen him forcibly administered ECT or subjected

1. The 20-foot stare in the 10-foot room, a fugue-like state frequently present in workers who winter-over in Antarctica (Roberts, 2011).

to psychosurgery, the fate of Jack Nicholson's 'McMurphy' in *One Flew Over the Cuckoo's Nest*. Time moves on, but doesn't necessarily progress. Donnie's treatment is we discover 'experimental'.

Wake up, I am watching you.

So begins Donnie's voyage of discovery, a 'prince ... led into a world of strange and beautiful magic' (Kelly, 2003: 23) that is the 'transient universe' – guided by the mysterious 'Frank', a menacing giant costumed rabbit whose hallucinated presence in the dark of night announces in slow deep base tones that 'the world is coming to an end' in '28 days, 6 hours, 42 minutes, 12 seconds' – the fate of the world counting down with no odd numbers in sight. Frank's presence summoning Donnie from his bed saves his life from a jet engine which has mysteriously fallen from the sky and crashed through the roof of his parents' home. Donnie's trip thus begins and like the wonderings of Bateson's (and Laing's) psychotic traveller it can 'only [be] completed by his return to the normal world, to which he comes back with insights different from those of the inhabitants who never embarked on such a voyage' (Bateson, 1961: xiii).

But who is Frank? In the original shooting script (Kelly, 2003: 10) Frank's initial greeting 'Helluva night for a walk' invites comparison with the autistic repetition of Arnold Schwarzenegger's cyborg killer (see French, 1996), whose naked presence in the Los Angeles streets of the same decade leads a group of resident punks to incant the almost identical phrase – duly repeated by Arnie; 'nice night for a walk'. The similarities do not end there; the Terminator like Frank (as we later learn) is on a mission from the future, Arnie's character has come to destroy the present-day world, while Frank's existence in the streets that never sleep is in some way necessary to save it. In both films, those who recognise the true intent of the respective time travellers are placed at the mercy of the local psychiatric constabulary. It is they who judge the appropriate response to the conundrum of such incomprehensible behaviour to be infusions of copious quantities of chlorpromazine plus – as we have seen in Donnie's case – a touch of psychoanalytically inspired talking. There are further allusions to another kind of terminator – the gas-inhaling, sociopathic Frank Booth of *Blue Velvet* whose threatening presence also turns the world of small town America upside down – and who eventually meets the same fate as the six-foot masked rabbit, a bullet in the face.

Donnie Darko premiered as the events of 9/11 ushered in an age of surveillance that would make Orwell blanch. Donnie has no faith in the drugs, even less in the small town bourgeois conventions that cement order in the suburban landscape he inhabits. Watchful eyes are everywhere – most notably from his aforementioned 'imaginary friend', who extols Donnie to commit various acts of wanton destruction to property. 'I can do anything I want … and so can you.' Donnie, who when it comes to destruction of property has previous form, obliges. First he floods the school after some carefully orchestrated action with spray paint and an axe. This finds its way into the sculptured bronzed head of the school mascot 'mongrel', resplendently defaced in the centre of the school grounds. Later, in an ecstatic orgy of arson, he burns down the house of Jim Cunningham (JC) (played by Patrick Swayze) – the smooth-talking, middle-aged community celebrity whose self-help brand of pseudo-psychological wisdom is dispensed via interactive 'lifeline' video exercises augmented by exuberant theatrical performance. He represents the paragon of responsibility, morality, and family values in Republican small town America – the representative person and the representative location so often for the elaboration of the American dream. But here in *Donnie Darko* – as the very title of the film implies – we are not dealing with dreams – but their flip side – nightmares. Liberalism, in the form of Dukakis, will be defeated; another term of Reaganism, spearheaded by George Bush looms on the horizon and the end of the world beckons, prefaced by the first Anglo-American attempt at sending Iraq back into the Stone Age. Ironic indeed that one of the global reflections of that war (the 9/11 attacks) haunts the initial release of the film.

If Donnie's thought processes are 'schizophrenic', Cunningham's own analytic framework is decidedly bipolar – the complexities of human existence reduced to a linear space bound by the twin poles of fear and love. The sum total of all human dilemmas must be captured within these confines – with the key to resolving them lying in the control of fear and the cultivation of appropriate 'attitudinal beliefs'. Cunningham is the archetypal 'one-dimensional man' (Marcuse, 1964) beset by a 'hardening of the categories' (e.g. Bannister & Fransella, 1971), his own and others' mental possibilities smothered beneath the unyielding range of convenience of a single construct. As Donnie might say of both the psychiatric and pseudo-psychological positions on display – 'life is not that simple'.

This lampooning of humanistic psychology stands in stark contrast to the apparent respect accorded to the psychiatric interventions (drug treatment, hypnosis and psychotherapy) on show. This despite evidence amongst young people of widespread non-adherence to antipsychotic medication (Townsend, Floersch & Findling, 2009) and a general unwillingness to seek out mental health services (Komiya, Good & Sherrod, 2000) – partly predicatable in both cases because of coercive treatment and the unpleasant side effects from the drugs (Day et al., 2005). Then there is the thorny issue of why a sixteen-year-old boy is being given powerful psychiatric drugs – something which predates Frank's sudden appearance in Donnie's life. One can only imagine they are being used as a 'method of behavioural control in children' who present with 'disruptive behaviour disorders' (Bentall, 2009: 240) with little care given to the potentially unknown and disastrous consequences of using them on a young developing person. Donnie's psychiatrist Dr Thurman appears to have bought into the ideology of pharmacology, influenced by the activities of the pharmaceutical industry in not only promoting their products for use with children – an area where the largest increases in prescription drugs have occurred – but in accepting the myth that any problems lie squarely within the individual rather than the way 'modern Western society has problematised childhood' (Moncrieff, 2008: 221), this when there is no shortage of evidence that the Middle American values running smack through the centre of Middlesex town are seriously up the creek.

It is as if the film has endorsed the relative status differentials in society between those who dispense psychological care and those who provide medical (psychiatric) 'care'. This is not to say that psychobabble itself does not constitute a legitimate target for mickey-taking – clearly it does – but quackery, in the guise of medicalising personal and social problems and disagreements, should not escape scot-free either. It is easy for the audience to side with this imbalance as Cunningham's house, following the inferno instigated by Donnie, is revealed as a veritable mansion of child pornography – a 'kiddie porn dungeon' as it is described in the film. Swayze thus makes the brave cinematic move from *Dirty Dancing* to 'dirty' pastimes in one fell swoop. Some of the 'respectable' residents of the town, chief amongst them one of Donnie's teachers, Ms Kitty Farmer, fearing the collapse of her moral universe, refuse to accept the 'horrible allegations' against Cunningham, alleging a conspiracy designed to 'destroy an innocent man' (Kelly, 2003: 80). Ms Falmer's unshakeable faith in the goodness and innocence of Jim Cunningham – an irrational belief resistant to counter-argument, not to mention her conspiracy theory – have an even less secure basis in reality than Donnie's belief in Frank and the impending demise of the world. Her motivated defence of the man she believes in is however not interpreted as delusional nor taken as evidence of an incipient psychosis – not even when combined with her further bizarre belief that the author and playwright Graham Greene is in fact the star of the old TV Western 'Bonanza'[2] and so she remains free to pursue her life unmolested by the psychiatric authorities. Her vision of the world is at one with the prevailing social norms set by adults. Donnie's questioning of the adult

---

2. The star of the series was in fact the actor Lorne Greene.

world, his earlier public denouncement of Cunningham as the 'Antichrist' and his visions are not. One recalls the cries of English playwright Nathaniel Lee on being committed to Bedlam, 'They called me mad, I called them mad, and damn them, they outvoted me' (cited in Porter, 2003: 88). In matters of the mind it often comes down to power – disciplinary power at that (Burr & Butt, 2000) – and in Donnie's world it is the adults who have it. On the role of power in deciding matters of sanity, psychiatric historian Roy Porter remarks, 'The issue is still alive' (2003: 88).

Cunningham is clearly a hypocrite, and deserves his just desserts – led away ignominiously by the police – while Dr Thurman is unquestionably sincere. There is no possibility of her indulging in the kind of abusive antics which Jeffrey Masson (1990) exposed as a disturbingly regular feature of mainstream mental health provision and which in recent times has been documented as part of the cultural repertoire of Catholic priests. Perhaps a reason for the differential respect shown to orthodox psychiatry as opposed to cod self-help lies in the fact that the audience do not really believe the ordinary members of the town require any psychological help at all whereas Donnie they believe clearly does have problems. He is we are told a 'paranoid schizophrenic'. He has visual and auditory command hallucinations, experiences temporal and spatial perception distortions, believes earnestly in the possibility of time travel – this conjoined to religious preoccupations about God and destiny – he believes himself to be on a special mission, imbued with special powers. Paradoxically his intellectual yearnings for a spiritual purpose to his life are prompted in part by his psychiatrist. Seen from the secure framework of our consensual reality we can appreciate why anyone in his world might consider him to be deluded. To cap it all he challenges authority both inside and outside the family and is also destructive of property – an exemplary case of oppositional defiant disorder, the psychiatric condition invented for the 4th edition of the *Diagnostic and Statistical Manual of Mental Disorders* (DSM-IV) (APA, 1994) for anybody who has a mind of their own!

Despite the enormity of the issues Donnie is grappling with however, he is recognised as a brilliant student with 'intimidating test scores' – none of the intellectual deterioration which is supposed to characterise schizophrenia – at its moment of creation considered a neurodegenerative condition, alleged to develop 'catastrophically in adolescence and early adult life' (Russell et al., 1997: 639). This should have alerted Donnie's psychiatrist to the inadequacy of the diagnosis; that it is there not to describe a hypothetical brain disorder allegedly shaping the young Mr Darko's life but to protect the psychiatrist from her own fears of Donnie – she simply cannot understand what he is talking about and so she fears him. She is not alone – Donnie's physics teacher Professor Kenneth

Monnitoff likewise beats a hasty retreat from any dialogue with him once Donnie's metaphysical speculations about the relationship of divinity to space–time travel are made known and provoke his own fears of losing his job. He too is held in liberal restraint by the same religious–conservative axis of fear. It is possible then that Cunningham might be right after all – fear is the key, not fear of one's emotions but institutional (psychiatric, educational and ecclesiastical) fear of others' personal autonomy – of anyone who dares to operate outside the box of what passes for normal socially sanctioned thought and behaviour.

The audience's appreciation of the fundamental decency of psychiatrist Lilian Thurman – irrespective of the quackery on which her profession is based – is rooted in their common fear of Donnie's 'psychopathology'. However the counterpoint to this is the audience's growing realisation that Donnie's 'mental health problems' reflect real issues and concerns which affect them and which in the fictional world on screen will have fatal consequences for the world if ignored. Donnie's actions in the world are reasoned and motivated but with the weight of the diagnosis around his neck any reasons he may have are spirited away on the psychiatric wind. This allows the town's residents, upset by his actions, to turn the spotlight away from their own intentions and flaws and avoid the liberation of self-doubt. As Szasz (2007b: 32) has pointed out 'one of the most important philosophical-political features of the concept of mental illness is that, at one fell swoop, it removes motivation from action, adds it to illness, and thus destroys the very possibility of separating disease from nondisease.' Cui bono? Not the patient!

Yes, we too are haunted by Frank, but we believe in him – his appearance is not an outcome of malfunctioning neurons, structural brain abnormalities or recalcitrant neurotransmitter levels in Donnie's brain. It is not, even as we first surmise, a manifestation of the sleep of reason in Donnie's mind – and like Donnie, perhaps more so, we fear him. In Frank (mistakenly as it turns out) we feel a tormenting evil presence – one of the seven princes of hell adrift in the late-twentieth century suburbia. Dr Thurman, too, senses the Leviathan, rationalising to herself and Donnie's parents that Frank represents a part of Donnie's subconscious mind – to her a part that can and ought to be pharmaceutically or otherwise shut down for her tranquillity as much as for Donnie's. She senses Frank is the harbinger of something that could engulf them all. Unable to control her own fear she employs her own psychiatric rhetoric to keep it at bay and dogmatically, if quietly, asserts that Donnie has lost contact with reality, a reality she assumes to know in its entirety. Who posits this as a response to his inability to control forces which he perceives to be threatening him, unaware all the while that the stultifying mores of the middle-class environment and her own role as an agent of social control and conformity are what truly threaten his liberty. It is Frank, in contrast, who provides him with a constant reminder of the fundamental reality of his existential condition – his freedom; he can do anything he wants – and Frank furthermore shows him the means (destruction of Cunningham's house) to expose a side of reality which is kept in society's subterranean caves.

Donnie wrestles continually with the horns of the free-will, determinism dilemma. He obeys Frank; he confides to Dr Thurman because he thinks he must – to him Frank has saved his life and that if he does not obey he will be left 'all alone' (Kelly, 2003: 87). Donnie's sister Elizabeth tries to tell him how the world in which they live is premised on dishonesty – that if you are too honest 'the world will eventually find a way to destroy you '(Kelly, 2003: 57). Paradoxically however, Donnie's choice to follow Frank's suggestions is ultimately revealed as necessary to uncover the truth of these people's lives and through this honesty (frankness) to save them all – hypocrites, pornographers, psychiatrists, narrow-minded teachers, Republicans et al. – something none of them can consciously comprehend. Donnie's inclinations to follow Frank's commands revolve around his own free will – he chooses to do so for what he believes is the greater good. His choosing thus preserves the integrity of our own moral choices. We alone are responsible for what we do – no higher power, whether alien or spiritual, no imagined entities, not our biochemistry. He is a young man with a mission – placed in the role of superhero. In our cynical psychiatrically dominated society such roles can only be claimed by those whom we deem to be psychotic. Nobody can be permitted to rail against the ills of the world or to champion their undoing unless we can earmark them as flawed, psychologically, preferably behaviourally flawed like all of us – in a manner which is taken to be normal, but which can attract our prurient disdain. And in our smug certainty certificated by state-sanctioned psychiatry, our view of reality – and as Szasz would opine in the therapeutic state there can be only one – absolutely must be endorsed by it.

But beyond this circle of closed minds are potential allies for Donnie – these include his father who maintains 'those people are full of shit' (Kelly, 2003: 73) and believes in Donnie's sanity. 'You aren't crazy,' he says. This is quite something coming from a parent who has been told by the psychiatric authorities that his son is mentally ill. Then there is Karen Pomeroy (Drew Barrymore[3]) 'the only good teacher here' who in class engages artfully, intelligently, even despairingly with him and with his

---

3. A younger Drew Barrymore of course encountered extraterrestrials in the movie *ET*. The audience can build on this identification of her as someone familiar with experiences which would normally attract psychiatric attention to increase the sense that she is sympathetic to Donnie.

girlfriend Gretchen. She is a newcomer to the town, her arrival precipitated by her stepfather's attempt to murder her mother. These three people in their own way, like Donnie, are misfits who won't follow society's rigid rules. There are costs for this; Donnie's father is threatened with divorce by his mother, Karen is eventually dismissed from her job for her pedagogical attempts to stir the creative minds of the students via the destructive fervour of Graham Greene's *The Destructors*, and Gretchen, like others at the school who wear their vulnerability on their sleeve, is subject to the taunts of those whose antics favour cruelty and humiliation. Gretchen provides for an interesting comparison with Dr Thurman for she too listens sympathetically to Donnie. Unlike Dr Thurman though she is able to acknowledge the frightening nature of his experiences, and attempts to provide some measure of reassurance not only in seeing Frank's presence as a meaningful sign but later in class mounting an impassioned defence of the (talking) rabbits of *Watership Down*. Like the six-foot Frank, one of these fictional rabbits has also prophesied impending catastrophe. They, as we, face ecological disaster. Like them we will not listen to prophesy. We only listen to prediction when, couched in the language of science, the predictions favour the accrual of further financial excess. Gretchen also amply demonstrates both Rogers' (1957) and Szasz's (1965/1988) proposition that supportive and empathic listening has nothing whatsoever to do with medicine; that it is not something that one acquires through a formal educational programme and is not something fundamentally different from what is present in all the other kinds of relationships that one may have in life.[4]

What is of great interest when considering this cast of allies and indeed Donnie too is that not one of them has chosen to adopt the reductionist biological language of the medical model. Neither Donnie, his father, mother, Gretchen or Karen consider him as 'mentally ill', 'schizophrenic' or 'psychotic'. Donnie instead describes himself as 'wacko' and as having 'emotional problems' and intones to his mother that 'there's nothing broken in my brain' (Kelly, 2003: 83) to which she herself responds, 'I know'. To Gretchen he is 'weird' – which from her is intended as a compliment (Kelly, 2003: 28) and as indicated above, to his father he is 'not crazy' at all. This triumph of lay language has considerable bearing on how Donnie's identity is depicted on the screen and on how fans of the film relate to his character. Donnie Darko's story appeals to many young people because his predicament – trying to make sense of existence, exploring independence, fearing aloneness, discovering love, rebellion, confusion and adult hypocrisy – are all issues they relate to. An alternative identity rooted in a potential career as zombified mental patient, courtesy

---

4. This philosophy is to be found in the practice of non-professional peer counselling (Kaufman & New, 2004).

of Dr Thurman and her like is not how they see him and this signals that the audience too is not convinced by the psychiatric word play on offer. The task for the audience when they leave the movie theatre or take back the rented DVD is to realise and apply this scepticism in their own lives.

The preference for these lay terms signals a communal resistance to the invasive project of psychiatric terminology – with its undeclared aim, the wholesale medicalisation of every facet of human behaviour. That such 'diagnostic imperialism' (Illich, 1977: 85) had failed to conquer the people of Middlesex is to the eternal credit of writer and director Richard Kelly. The film's release came hot on the heels of the 'decade of the brain' (1990–2000) – spearheaded by President Bush in 1990 (Bush, 1990) as a 'new era of discovery' in 'brain research' specifically intended to further entrench the view of depression, anxiety and schizophrenia as 'brain disorders' (http://www.loc.gov/loc/brain/). That so many characters in this film refuse to endorse this perspective suggests at the very least that some sections of society remain highly sceptical, not only of the claims advanced by the champions of biological psychiatry but also of the very wisdom of a project which if successful would lead to a wholesale replacement of the philosophical and ethical problems of human living with a medical metaphor and an insurance bill. Kelly himself is on record lamenting the overzealous drugging (usually with Ritalin) of young people. He is cautious in his words – a wise move given the hostile reception meted out to A-list actor Tom Cruise for his outspoken criticisms of psychiatry as pseudoscience.

The cast of misfits is completed by the enigmatic and reclusive Roberta Sparrow – 'Grandma Death' as she is otherwise known – an 'old crazy woman' and former nun who we learn had 'changed overnight … and became an entirely different person' (Kelly, 2003: 47). She has turned from religion to science. In the film she is the author of *The Philosophy of Time Travel*, a strange illustrated book lent to Donnie by his physics teacher which seems to not only describe the kind of unusual and bizarre experiences he is having – but also the phenomenology and *raison d'être* of what she refers to as the 'tangent universe'. This book provides context and meaning, an explanation for Donnie's mission in the world since the appearance of Frank. If he can unravel the mystery of the book then he can understand what is happening to himself. Therein is the implied suggestion that Roberta Sparrow must herself have previously encountered the same splitting of the world, and like Donnie, found herself cast out of the primary reality into an alternate version of the world, chosen for reasons unknown to prevent the world we know from collapsing out of existence.

The Philosophy of Time Travel presents itself as 'a simple and direct guide in a time of great danger', a treatise on how to act when a physical instability in the primary universe, generated from the corrupting effects of war, plague, famine and natural disaster, leads to the creation of an alternative reality capable of destroying the primary one. Sparrow's work describes what actions must be taken to return the world to its state before the inception of the breakaway world. There is little doubt that the Roberta Sparrows of this world, like the Donnie's Darkos, would have the content of their thinking ignored – and used only in psychiatric parlance to assign it to the 'correct category' of paranoid delusional thinking. Kelly's plea throughout the film is for tolerance toward these loners, misfits, eccentrics and rebels. What if people feel they have a special purpose in life? Doesn't it make good psychological sense to think so? In the radical psychiatric world modelled on Darwinian principles, we are not permitted to think this – all explicitly expressed purposes are delusions – tricks the 'evolved' mind plays on us, including the idea that we are, ipso facto, moral agents. Of course when scientific, industrial and military action proceeds on this basis people invariably find themselves on the receiving end of immoral acts. Why then can we not tolerate such a sense of purpose or people whose ideas seem widely out of sync with our own? Why can't such people be left to live their lives as they wish? It is rank arrogance to imagine that we who believe in an ordered state-sanctioned psychiatrically ordained reality, necessarily understand that reality best.

Kelly's masterwork on first reading appears to reject the totality offered by a material discursive account of existence. In the director's cut of the film Dr Thurman confesses to Donnie that his pills have been placebo's at once signalling both the psychiatrist's own lack of faith in the medicine she peddles and her penchant for deception – the twin pillars on which the discipline has so frequently been taken to task. 'Kindness and lies' wrote Graham Greene (2001: 48) – who knew something of psychiatry as well as Catholicism – 'are worth a thousand truths' – a succinct summary of what appears to be on offer from Dr Thurman. Indeed the pills do not work (Moncrieff, 2008) and that psychiatry is no more than a 'science of lies' (Szasz, 2008) is becoming increasingly apparent, hence the legitimacy of psychiatry is under threat as never before. The response to this threat is to medicalise everything in sight while it is still possible – akin to the spending spree of a departing government which has lost its mandate.

In an interview Kelly (2003: xxix) maintains that this depiction of Dr Thurman argues for her belief in Donnie's sanity – that he is 'not crazy'. However Kelly's own interpretation here cannot be trusted, having already had Dr Thurman describe Donnie as suffering from 'paranoid schizophrenia'. What his comments do give us however is further evidence of the ambivalence and confusion surrounding the public representations of psychiatry not least in terms of what we expect, what we want and what we actually get from psychiatrists. What we want is love, hope, respect, listening and support, what we expect is usually something less, but at least some recognition of the human struggle we are embroiled in, and what we usually get are drugs, scant conversation and the pharmaceutically sponsored mumbo jumbo of chemical imbalances. In the persona of Katharine Ross's kindly Dr Thurman, Donnie experiences the full gamut of these possibilities. Of course had the school authorities ever discovered that a non-drugged Donnie took an axe to their property while under her supervision then it is likely that she would find herself on the receiving end of a law suit. By such means do psychiatrists sometimes become victims of the power they have campaigned to have invested in them!

As the film heads towards its denouement, evidence mounts that the events unfolding in Middlesex do so at the behest of a 'higher power'. Given the religious iconography on display – Donnie's suspicions that he is acting in accordance with the wishes of heavenly forces are rational and comprehensible. And on first viewing, the theatrical release of the film hints at a hidden divine hand orchestrating events in the tangent universe. The director's cut however presents a slightly different interpretation – the erstwhile higher power is now, with some subtlety, imagined as an advanced technological presence ensuring the correct resolution of fate. In the commentary to the film Kelly acknowledges either interpretation as valid – though the visuals employed – reminiscent of Schwarzenegger's mind's eye computational gymnastics in *The Terminator* suggest that the power above is more intelligent technology than spiritual intelligence. But were such an advanced intelligence capable of this degree of manipulation to exist, it would surely be seen by many of us as possessing god-like powers. This perhaps is Kelly's point in supporting both a divine and technological reading. In the movie the spiritual/technological master plan which underpins the apparent absurdity of life (a master plan which guides Frank and Gretchen to Donnie, impels all of Donnie's wayward acts, and places his mother on the plane whose defective engine will crash into the primary universe) is one which cannot be discerned by teachers of physics, healers of the mind, nuns, or conservative ideologues. It is the mystery of being which *Donnie Darko* the film and the character celebrates. Contrast this with the opening pages of the psychiatric bible (the DSM) which premises the very notion of psychiatric disorders on the basis of what does or does not constitute an expectable response to an event – as if the sum total of all expectable responses to the sum total of all possible events could ever be known in advance and read off a psychiatric checklist. *Donnie Darko* stands in opposition to such thought. Do we know how people 'ought' to respond, given the infinite variety of ways in which people can undergo distress and trauma? Of course we do not and hence the very idea of psychological medicine is in principle absurd.

As the clock counts down to the prophesied moment of destruction, Donnie and Gretchen scour Roberta Sparrow's house in the hope of finding her or discerning at this late hour some further critical clue to the mystery enveloping them. Unsuccessful they instead find themselves assaulted by two of their delinquent (masked) classmates. In the melee which ensues Gretchen is accidentally run over and killed by a car driven to the scene by a young man in a rabbit costume. It is a fully incarnate Frank, who Donnie realises he must now kill – and does so by shooting him in the face – in order that Frank can fulfil his destiny as a messenger in the tangent universe. He is one of the manipulated dead, described in Roberta Sparrow's book as one who can help him guide the 'artefact' (the fallen jet engine in Donnie's world) back to the primary universe and hence save the world. With Gretchen dead and morning about to break, Donnie engineers the creation of the time portal to his house at the precise moment he was originally summoned by Frank. Thus, as a cinematic (allegedly) psychotic superhero, he 'seizes the day', returns through the portal, and saves the world from destruction in an act which only he can be cognisant of. His life ends, killed by the engine from the tangent universe crashing into his bedroom. Having come to the realisation that the master plan is now completed he sacrifices himself so that life for others (sinners such as Jim Cunningham even) can continue. Donnie then is simultaneously a Christ figure and superhero (though the man in the mask more normally denoting superheroes is Frank) – both categories of person – who should they actually appear in the modern world, crown of thorns or utility belt in tow, would unquestionably find themselves sectioned and their mental health credentials revoked. Being a force for the common good or a superhero doesn't carry much weight outside the cinema. In response to Brian Patten's poetic lament 'Where are you now Batman?' (Henri, McGough & Patten, 1974: 113), the twenty-first century custodians of our sanity would no doubt sadly inform us that the caped crusader (and any other of his ilk) had been sectioned under the Mental Health Act, drugged out of his Bat suit, another victim of benevolent psychiatric intolerance.

Concluding comments

Donnie Darko is replete with themes of modern angst, symbolically dense and like any good dream richly determined. It is a disaster movie with a twist – the disaster isn't a disaster! A plethora of movies in the last two decades resonate with fears of economic, ecological and planetary collapse, drawing their impetus from a dimly felt fear of impending catastrophe; *Donnie Darko* is different. If its plot and dramatic setting are suffused with these tensions, the suggestion of an approaching doomsday is deliciously but ironically turned on its head with the message that 'everything is going to be just fine' (Kelly, 2003: 100). This is not necessarily there to provide banal reassurance in the face of potentially catastrophic change, but a realisation that collapse of this disturbed, illiberal society may just be as Voltaire, (1947: 20) imagined, 'all ... for the best'. A future sensibility which gives greater credence to questioning normal experience of the world, which does not shun alternative takes on reality nor the varieties of experience of which the human animal is capable (Laing, 1967; Cardeña, Lynn & Krippner, 2000), which accepts and celebrates difference, is one to be welcomed, and we may have to go through a 'storm' to attain it. Donnie's apparent madness is not the breakdown it seems, but an attempt to make sense of a world in crisis. Amidst the decaying infrastructure of the postmodern capitalist metropolis, psychiatry, allied with the conservative forces of the state, has accepted the role of policeman. This is not the friendly bobby on the beat, but a frenzied disciplinarian who is as likely to dish out a thrashing as point you in the direction of home.

In the maelstrom of change, *Donnie Darko* suggests that familiar havens of thought – religion, education, politics, and psychiatry – provide no sanctuary. These belong to a way of life – our way of life – which is imperilled by an inability to understand and respond appropriately to the damaging changes for which they are responsible. At the beginning of the twenty-first century we have already embarked on a prolonged period of social, cultural, economic and environmental upheaval. The 'shock of the new' that is coming stands to erode old intellectual landmarks. What will replace them will be strange and unfamiliar, and will simultaneously and urgently demand from us the desire and flexibility to 'question mom and dad's rules' (Kelly, 2003: 85). *Donnie Darko* can therefore be seen not as a rallying cry for belief in the supernatural but as a morality play about liberty and destiny, posing fundamental questions about the choices unleashed by natural forces and their collision with a redundant hypocritical society (Jones, 2005). How do we exercise freedom against a backdrop of inevitable change? We do not live like Donnie Darko in a theatre of dreams under the twin gaze of psychiatry and a giant rabbit; the stage upon which we strut our stuff, permeated with 24/7 surveillance and Big Brother, does not end when the curtain drops or the credits cease. Like the eponymous hero of this film we too find ourselves adrift in turbulent waters and, like him, 'time' may be 'almost up' (Kelly, 2003: 88) for us to make our choices. Donnie Darko was ultimately the master of his fate; who, in the days ahead, will be the captain of our soul?

Chapter Four

A Beautiful Mind: Pharmaceutical secrets and lies

My name's John Nash. I'm being held against my will.

Ron Howard's Oscar-winning drama loosely based on Sylvia Nasar's (1998) biography of Nobel Prize[1] winning mathematician John Forbes Nash Jr. brings to the fore a multitude of concerns. These relate not just to Nash's character and his location in the socioeconomic, political and cultural milieu of his time or the respective values accorded to unfeeling thinking and unthinking feeling in Western societies, important as these are, but also and more particularly to the pernicious and extensive influence of the mental health and pharmaceutical industries on public perceptions and consciousness. Whilst the representations of gender and class relations, mental health, psychiatric treatment, psychiatric power and state power on display in this production merit serious attention, the one issue which overrides all of these and which must be considered a priori is one of truth telling. Had there been an academy award available for this, *A Beautiful Mind* would most certainly not have been nominated. The litany of lies and half truths which the viewer must contend with rivals anything to be found in the sterling imagination of Jorge Luis Borges, and can arguably be said to begin with the very title of the picture.

While the elegance, originality and brilliance of Nash's mathematical work cannot be doubted we are being asked to accept that the 'beauty' of his mathematical insights extends beyond the sphere of intellectual calculation and serves as an apt description of his entire mind. Yet in order to accept this, even if only in a poetic sense, one must either throw all knowledge of Nash's personality overboard or else view his personhood as synonymous with the 'identity' accorded a rational calculating machine – a proposition both preposterous and dehumanising. Even before Nash's psychological breakdown at the age of thirty (in 1959) his behaviour was characteristically very socially unskilled, selfish,

---

1. The prize awarded to Nash, 'The Central Bank of Sweden Prize in Economic Science in Memory of Alfred Nobel' is strictly speaking not a 'true' Nobel Prize. These are awarded, as stipulated in the will of Alfred Nobel, only for work in physics, chemistry, medicine, literature and peace. The prize in economics has in fact had a somewhat controversial history, with occasional calls from within the science community for its abolition. Since Nash won it in 1994, it has been transformed into an award open to all the social sciences.

arrogant, aggressive, rude, cold, cruel, mean and on occasion some have argued racist. Nash as understood by his colleagues 'had no affect' (Nasar, 1998: 73), was 'often oblivious to the feelings and motivations of other people' (ibid: 94), had a 'social IQ of 12' (ibid: 101), 'didn't care whether [his] students learned or not' (ibid: 138), and was not someone for whom people 'felt any warmth' (ibid: 72). He was in short 'immune to the emotional forces that bind people together' (ibid: 167).

These facets of Nash's personality, far from the realms of beauty, are as much a part of who he is as is his extraordinary mathematical ability. Though today they would most likely attract a diagnosis along the autistic spectrum[2] they are important considerations in contextualising the aptness of his employment at the RAND Corporation, the US think-tank where facts 'preferably detached from emotion' (Nasar, 1998: 109) were put to work to service the US military machine by dreaming 'up new ways to wage wars and keep enemies at bay' (Abella, 2008). The principal intellectual instrument used in this endeavour was game theory, originally the brainchild of John von Neumann (von Neumann & Morgenstern, 2007) and subsequently extended in its power and complexity by Nash – for which he was to receive the Nobel Prize. Game theory was developed to address and hopefully 'solve' an array of theoretical, strategic, interpersonal, national and military problems (Coleman, 1982) and was considered to be 'RAND's secret weapon in a nuclear war of wits against the Soviet Union' (Nasar, 2007: xx). Nash confessed to colleagues that as a child he had enjoyed 'torturing animals' (ibid: 37). As an adult his game theory ideas would play a part in manufacturing the global (and domestic) balance of terror in the Cold War with the Soviet Union. This distasteful backdrop is almost completely absent from the vision of socially awkward tortured genius which director Ron Howard offers up for consumption, and it is absent for a very good reason. The 'beautiful mind' served up by Howard is an upgrade from his earlier *Forest Gump*. Whereas Gump lumbered through the wasteland of the Vietnam War, the napalming of civilians airbrushed out for convenience, we have Nash wandering through the urban jungle of the Cold War, neither man capable of anything beyond servitude to the prevailing political economic zeitgeist. In both cases the 'beautiful mind' being adorned belongs neither to Gump nor Nash, but references the rational calculating mode of living that is the philosophy guiding the

---

2. That this is so should not be taken to imply either the validity of, or support for, the medicalisation of behaviour. What is important in the context of Nash's behaviour is that people with the marked social deficiencies which attract the Asperger's label find themselves frequently subject to criticism from others and being made fun of – the response to which Wing (1981) notes may be mistaken for a paranoid psychosis, the diagnosis which Nash was later to receive. Those who are preoccupied with abstract theories or their own imaginary world may be mistakenly said to have delusions.

modus operandi of US imperial capitalism (Curtis, 2007). It gives rise to the world we observe today – a world seemingly without meaning or purpose beyond the continuation of the existing capitalist oligarchy.

These same values also underpin our evaluation of genius – a preference in the sciences for the safety and elegance of formal rigour above real-world validity. The successful development of formal theory in the sciences however can only lead to a successful understanding of reality if theory heeds the responses from the real world that come from its application. But the failures of both psychiatric 'theory' and economic 'theory', Nash's mathematical models of social interaction amongst the latter, lie precisely in the studied neglect of this contract between theory and reality. Experimental tests of game theory for example had already revealed that the behaviour of 'players' did not conform to the selfish predictions of economic theory with each person seeking to 'maximise their utilities'. John Milnor, for example, a colleague of Nash's at Princeton, questioned the central assumptions of game theory; 'The hypothesis ... that all of the players are rational, that they understand the precise rules of the game, and that they have complete information about the objectives of all the other players ... this is seldom completely true' (cited in Nasar, 2007: 150). He went on to say that Nash's theory, the product of his 'keen beautiful logic mind' was 'not realistic as a descriptive theory' as it neglected 'the psychology of the players and the mechanism of their interaction'.

For many economists however the lack of psychological reality in Nash's work was irrelevant – for them the formal elegance of the calculations produced a mathematical utopia which, sufficient unto itself, echoed their own belief in the workings of the free market. If reality is unfortunate enough not to conform to economic speculation then it must be (violently) engineered to fit free market theory – through the economic shock therapy (Klein, 2007) of the IMF and World Bank-led structural adjustment programmes if necessary, rather than the other way round. In the use of violence to extort validation for its bankrupt ideas economics has much in common with psychiatry. In recent years, when interviewed by filmmaker Adam Curtis, Nash himself conceded that 'the human as businessman' in these models 'has little connection with the complexity of real human beings' who are 'not entirely motivated by self-interest' (Curtis, 2007) and that becoming aware of this 'overdependence on rationality' was for him a form of 'enlightenment!' Sadly, Nash's elevation to the spiritual plane does nothing to alter the course of an economic 'science' which was long ago hijacked by the rich and powerful to steer the world economy through an ocean of self-interest. The types of selfish human behaviour which are axiomatic in much economic theory are in actuality systematically observed in only two groups of people – economists and psychopaths (Curtis, 2007), with the operating principles of the latter legally enshrined in the precepts governing the day-to-day workings of the typical Anglo-American corporation, in which the notion of social responsibility is nothing more than an 'oxymoron' (Bakan, 2005: 101).

Nash's liberation from the limited perspective which directed his interpersonal, occupational and professional behaviour was won at a very severe cost. *A Beautiful Mind* does not present Nash's life as a narrative of liberation from his own emotional shortcomings, ultimately giving way to an enhanced appreciation of human virtues and an increased questioning of the inherent values in the national corporate psyche. Instead we see a degraded 'epic' of an American hero who managed to overcome the burden of mental illness through the help of a devoted wife, aided and abetted by caring psychiatric authorities. This necessarily leaves unquestioned the causes of Nash's apparent psychological meltdown and the significance of the wider cultural milieu in it. It is therefore important that we examine in some detail how the film deals with these issues, beginning with Nash's entry to Princeton and his mental breakdown.

The opening credits introduce us to the intellectual hothouse of Princeton in 1947. They are barely over before we have been forewarned of the Soviet desire for global domination and instructed in the welcoming speech to students that 'mathematicians won the [Second World] war'. As we catch our first glimpse of a youthful John Nash (Russell Crowe) the new intake are challenged to consider 'who among' them 'will be the vanguard of freedom, democracy and discovery?' The message is unmistakable and didactic; whatever mathematics John Nash will do in this or any other establishment will serve the greater good – our greater good. Three minutes into the film and already there can be no possibility that the values which course through the veins of elite institutions will be open to question. Their values are ours even if we didn't know it. A further two minutes into the proceedings and we have been introduced to roommate 'Charles Herman', who seems real enough to the casual observer but as it later transpires is apparently an hallucinatory manifestation of Nash's supposed 'schizophrenia'. Whatever difficulties and problems the real John Nash endured, visual hallucinations did not figure amongst them.

By means of this plot device, substituting the visual realm for the ideational, the film not only shows its disdain for dealing with the substance of Nash's problematic beliefs but also displays its ignorance on matters which are of considerable importance to understanding both the subject and the subject matter of the movie.[3] In the commentary to the

---

3. It is also noteworthy that the chronology of the movie plays fast and loose with the facts of Nash's life in suggesting he was already 'mentally ill' when he entered Princeton in 1947. As indicated earlier his breakdown did not occur for a further 12 years. As such the film suggests the events of these 12 years are irrelevant to understanding Nash's later state of mind.

film, director Ron Howard and screenwriter Akiva Goldsman repeatedly describe these 'hallucinations' as delusions. We have Howard for example incessantly referring to 'delusional characters' and 'informing' us that delusions are 'primarily auditory' phenomena, whilst in turn Goldsman refers to Nash 'talking to his delusions' – highlighting an inadequate understanding on both their parts of what these terms actually mean. This is no trivial point. It is much simpler to question and indeed establish beyond any doubt the veracity or otherwise of a visual perception – that is whether it derives from concurrent external stimuli or not – than it is to delve into the thorny issue of what constitutes a delusionary belief (David, 1999). The DSM defines these as false beliefs, not normally accepted by other members of one's culture and resistant to contrary evidence or reasoned arguments. As has been well recognised however, almost all of these features can be found in so-called 'normal' beliefs – Tony Blair's 'belief' in the presence of weapons of mass destruction in Iraq being a case in point.

Goldsman however, like Sylvia Nasar, has signed up to a disease-centred view of Nash's problems without realising the difficulties and confusion this creates. For example during one scene where Nash is seen physically struggling with (the imaginary) Charles, Goldsman remarks that the 'truth of this disease [is that] if seen from the inside it [Nash's thinking and behaviour] would seem quite reasonable or understandable'. In saying this however Goldsman has signed up to the nonsensical view that a supposed organic pathological disease process may have motives! He then compounds this by identifying the aims and intentions of the sinister 'Parcher', another of Nash's hallucinatory characters, with the hypothetical disease process itself. 'Parcher,' he says, 'will serve to challenge him, invite him in and ultimately reject him as the illness often does.' Interviewed after the film in 2004 by Marika Griehself,[4] Nash was adamant that the film 'does not describe accurately the nature of the delusional thinking which was my history'. So of what exactly did Nash's delusional thinking consist, how was it represented in the film and what was the context in which it emerged and evolved? These issues will now be addressed.

The sum total of Nash's 'psychosis' is represented in the film through the presence of several hallucinatory characters (Parcher, Charles, Charles' niece – a young girl Marcee,[5] and anonymous individuals who at different points in the narrative are either following or pursuing Nash), together with his 'imagined' activity participating in a 'top secret ... endeavour' in

---

4. The interview can be accessed at http://nobelprize.org/mediaplayer/index.php?id=429

5. There according to Goldsman to represent 'faith, unconditional love and purity'. Jennifer Connelly as Nash's wife Alicia in the film obviously lacks these in sufficient quantity.

which his 'code-breaking' skills are put to use, finding hidden codes and patterns supposedly 'embedded in newspapers and magazines' by a faction of the Soviet Red Army intent on smuggling a nuclear weapon into the US and detonating it. As Parcher becomes more insistent and 'threatening' this plotline is used to provide narrative context for Nash's growing isolation, secretiveness and suspiciousness. These are the manifestations of his 'paranoia' which lead to him being admitted against his will to a psychiatric hospital, the rite of passage to psychiatric Neverland supervised courtesy of an injection of Thorazine by the lead psychiatric figure in the film – a Dr Rosen. The fictional Rosen is not to be mistaken for the actual John Rosen, pioneer of direct psychoanalysis, who lost his licence to practise psychiatry following the revelation of his widespread physical and sexual abuse of patients (Masson, 1990). Nash's *cri de coeur*, as he is being subdued, that Rosen is a Russian spy, is accompanied in the screenwriter's commentary by the curious remark that 'we', the audience 'are constantly left wondering whether or not this man (Dr Rosen) is a psychiatrist or a spy'.

Rather than showing the fictional Nash's belief as absurd or irrational – as the supposed outcome of the disease process that the screenwriter and director believe in – the film presents it, given the circumstances, as reasoned and reasonable. This is yet another indication that the filmmakers think psychiatric 'illnesses' as opposed to physical illnesses have motives. Mental illness for them must perforce amount to conduct governed by motives we (or rather they) do not like. This is of course precisely what Thomas Szasz argues does lie behind ascriptions of mental illness. Howard and Goldsman thus unwittingly show us that psychiatrists will detain persons against their will even when said persons have understandable and reasonable beliefs. Subsequent to Nash's forced removal from the campus his protestations as he is being strong-armed by two hospital orderlies, *'My name's John Nash. I'm being held against my will'* are described by Goldsman as evidence that Nash is in the grip of a 'classic paranoid delusion'. But Nash – even in the context of the film *is* being held against his will. It cannot therefore be a false belief. Goldsman is obviously highly confused, more confused, it must be said, than the fictional Nash at this point.

In a further revealing commentary Goldsman informs us that the sequence in which Nash is apparently dropping secret communications to his handler (Parcher) was edited just after the events of 9/11, which had the effect of rendering the notion of agents of foreign powers operating on US soil suddenly 'so much more real' for him. If Goldsman really required 9/11 to bring this to his attention he must be heavily indoctrinated. Of course belonging to the elite film-making Hollywood community insulates Goldsman from the possibility that his belief structure –

seriously at odds with reality – will be designated delusional. Goldsman elaborates, 'The insidious nature of paranoid delusion creates in the mind of the person who suffers, rational, reasonable explanations for ... what the sufferer sees.' The obvious trouble with this errant nonsense is that this is precisely the manner in which everyone's mind works – whether delusional or not! Perception is hypothesis and rationale (Gregory, 1966). The fictional Nash simply cannot win. He is said to be delusional if he maintains he is being held against his will when in fact he undoubtedly is and also when he believes that agents of foreign powers are operating on US soil which of course they do (see Cornwell, 2010 for a recent example) just as US agents are of course operative on the soil of foreign powers. In their attempts to depict the insanity of the fictional John Nash the film-makers unintentionally show the reasonableness of Nash's views and the unreasonableness of their own. They of course, like psychiatrists, have the power to define reality for others – even if the definition is incoherent. An important question now is whether the real John Nash fared any better than his fictional counterpart. How does the fictional 'psychosis' compare to the behaviour and experience of the real John Nash? To address this we must first provide a background sketch of the context of Nash's actual life.

Nash's mathematical career began at Carnegie where because of his social difficulties, he was, on the admission of other students there, 'ostracised', 'teased' and 'tormented' (Nasar, 1998: 42). From there he moved to Princeton for his doctoral work, where 'starved of affection' (ibid: 101) he encountered both Albert Einstein and the architect of game theory John von Neumann. Von Neumann, who worked on the Manhattan Project and advocated a nuclear first strike against the Soviet Union, was it is argued the template for Stanley Kubrick's mad scientist Dr Strangelove. Exuding a heady mixture of 'charm', 'wit' and calculating coldness, the widespread joke was that he was 'really an extra-terrestrial who had learned how to imitate a human perfectly'(Nasar, 1998: 80). Despite von Neumann's apparent predilection to favour US aggression, along with Einstein and other prominent intellectuals of the time, including Bertrand Russell and John Maynard Keynes, he shared a belief in the necessity of world government in order to solve the problems of political conflict in the beckoning nuclear era – 'the only salvation for civilization and the human race' wrote Einstein (Pais, 1982: 474). Von Neumann and his work exerted an immense influence on Nash, this influence travelling with him to the RAND Corporation[6] where he worked as a consultant for several years (1950–1954), at the height of both the Cold War, and the deep democratic freeze of the McCarthyist era (Kuhn & Nasar, 2001). Once there, Nash, a socially awkward, inept and psychologically ostracised individual, found

---

6. Not the Pentagon as depicted in the film.

himself embroiled in the RAND world of geopolitical conspiracy and obsession, with its 'weirdly compelling mix of Olympian detachment, paranoia and megalomania' (Nasar, 1998: 104). When he moved to MIT, the mathematics department there was said to be in a 'state of siege' (ibid: 152), under threat from a cavalcade of McCarthyist-inspired FBI investigators. This combination of state–corporate-mediated anti-communist paranoia and intellectually supported peacemaking comprised the experiential world in the United States at that time which for Nash and his colleagues was culturally, politically and professionally rationalised and normalised. Into this mix must be considered the further psychological stresses to arise from Nash's homosexual liaisons (considered grounds for denying security clearance in the defence industry at the time) and his arrest for an alleged homosexual misdemeanour in a public toilet (indecent exposure). The latter led to the cancellation of his contract with RAND and the revoking of his security clearance. This in turn led to his forced isolation from the group of intellectuals he had worked with for several years. Nash has attributed his own difficulties to several factors: the challenges engendered by his wife Alicia's pregnancy, the difficulties brought on by working on the Riemann hypothesis,[7] his attempts to resolve the contradictions in quantum theory,[8] the stresses of teaching and his desire for recognition. There are also the additional factors to be considered of his possible use of steroids (Nasar, 1998: 174) as well as the far from simple act of managing his relationship with his first son from an earlier liaison.

When Nash's behaviour moved sufficiently beyond the norms of his wife and colleagues and led to Alicia having him incarcerated,[9] Nasar (1998) instructs us that his delusional outpourings included the declaration that he was 'the emperor of Antarctica' (ibid: 239), that he 'believed he was on the verge of cosmic insights' (ibid: 18), that his 'career was being ruined by aliens from outer space' (ibid: 243), that he was being 'bugged' and 'wrote strange letters to the United Nations' (ibid: 248), as well as 'various foreign ambassadors, the pope [sic], even the FBI' (ibid: 249), that 'NATO, Warsaw, Middle East and SEATO pact[10] countries' were 'threats to world peace' (ibid: 273), and that there was a 'conspiracy amongst military leaders to take over the world' (ibid: 258). And to cap it

---

7. 'One of the greatest unsolved problems in pure mathematics' (Nasar, 1998: 18) and regarded by some as 'a dangerous area to go into' (ibid: 232).
8. He described these as 'psychologically destabilising' (Nasar, 1998: 221).
9. Nash's wife Alicia had him committed several times. On each occasion this was against his will.
10. The Southeast Asia Treaty Organisation (SEATO) was brought into being in 1954, its members included the UK, US, Australia, France, New Zealand, Thailand, Pakistan, The Philippines, Taiwan, South Korea and South Vietnam. SEATO's creation, a consequence of the Truman Doctrine, was intended to function as a series of anti-communist bilateral and collective defence treaties (http://en.wikipedia.org/wiki/Southeast_Asia_Treaty_Organization).

all off, Nash was talking of 'going to Europe' to try and 'form a world government' (ibid: 260). Once hospitalised his view that he 'was a political prisoner' (ibid: 260) was taken as further evidence of delusional thinking. Other aspects of Nash's behaviour which were construed as evidence of his insanity concern a variety of word plays and arcane messages which he scribbled on various blackboards around the campus – which earned him the title of the 'Phantom of Fine Hall' and which it seems 'nobody' professed to understand (ibid: 332).

Whilst these examples of Nash's 'strange' behaviour are by no means exhaustive they are certainly more than sufficient to be illustrative. Do they however make sense – or do they constitute prima facie evidence that Nash had 'lost his grip on reality' as the fictional and non-fictional psychiatrists maintained? Psychiatrists it must be said do not always make for good poets or make good sense of poetic metaphor when they encounter it.[11] A lack of appreciation of the playful character of language is a serious, perhaps fatal, omission in any enterprise which seeks to understand the human condition and it is a necessary prerequisite for any attempt to comprehend Nash's plight. Many if not all of the above examples are either metaphorically true or directly true. First the straightforward: it should by now, from any dispassionate reading of world history, be incontrovertible that the NATO, Warsaw, Middle East and SEATO pact alliances are/were threats to peace as Nash declared. That military leaders have been instrumental in taking over large parts of the world in defiance of the democratic wishes of the citizens there (e.g. in Nash's day, Chile, Indonesia, Korea, Vietnam and Algeria should suffice as a few relevant examples) often with the direct support of Nash's home country, the United States, is also incontrovertible.

Moving to the more poetic, Nash's description of himself as the 'emperor of Antarctica' provides an eloquent example of the fruits to be realised from combining poetic imagery with personal insight. Similarly his claim that his 'career was being ruined by aliens from outer space' is not unintelligible. On the contrary it is easily intelligible if a modicum of effort is expended. His pioneering work in game theory was ill received by von Neumann, who 'didn't think much of Nash's breakthrough' and 'dismissed it' as 'trivial' (Nasar, 2007: xix) – this being the same von Neumann, the towering intellect of Princeton, who as indicated earlier, was widely referred to as 'an extra-terrestrial who had learned how to imitate a human perfectly' (Nasar, 1998: 80). His belief that he was close to 'cosmic insights' should also be considered plausible given his stupendous

---

11. Perhaps there is a need for their medical training to be combined with courses in language and literature!

mathematical ability which was applied in cosmology amongst other areas – an area which Nash has continued to work in since resuming his career in later life. His desire to form a world government may not have stood much chance of success but this again was an idea which enjoyed respect and currency in intellectual high places. On this reading Nash is guilty of nothing more than using metaphorical discourse and action in socially unconventional ways in order to convey his unhappiness with himself and the world. As Laing (1965: 31) put it 'one may see his behaviour as "signs" of a "disease" or one may see his behaviour as expressive of his existence.' It is Nash's misfortune that it was seen by Alicia Nash and the psychiatric fraternity as the former. Many, though certainly not all of his mathematical colleagues – accustomed to the eccentricities and peculiarities of what a seat at the high table of the mathematical community entails – considered him to be no more than eccentric if a little difficult.

One example of Nash's 'unusual' writing provides an amusing example of how he was thinking and what he thought of those who wield power and wage war. Nasar (1998: 333) relates how shortly after Heisuke Hironaka had won the Fields Medal[12] for a proof relating to mathematical singularities,[13] one of Nash's messages (during the 1970s) read:

$$N^5 + I^5 + X^5 + O^5 + N^5 = 0$$

Can Hironaka resolve this singularity?

As an adult Nixon was the fifth President of the United States Nash would have experienced (following Truman, Eisenhower, Kennedy and Johnson). Here we see each letter in Nixon's name raised to the fifth power and Nixon equated to nothing or perhaps singled out amongst inhabitants of the Oval Office as one of a kind – which given his involvement in the Watergate affair and illegal bombing of Cambodia he undoubtedly was. In asking whether Hironaka can resolve (make sense of) this Nash could well be pointing to the limitations of mathematics, the inability of understanding the world through mathematical analysis alone, and if so he is surely right. As a marriage of mathematical poetry and political critique this is exceptional, not delusional.

Nash, involuntarily confined, was on the receiving end of the typical psychiatric armoury of the 1950s – major tranquillisers (Thorazine) and

---

12. The Fields Medal, considered the highest honour in mathematics, is awarded every four years.
13. In mathematics, a singularity is in general a point at which a given mathematical object is not defined, or fails to be well-behaved in some particular way, that is when equations do not give a valid value. A simple example is $f(x)=1/x$ when $x=0$.

insulin shock therapy – which to the film's credit is presented realistically and accurately in what is a quite brutal scene. Speaking of his hospital stay, Nash told students and colleagues, 'they had everything', except 'freedom' (Nasar, 1998: 264). The movie suggests that Nash received shock treatment five times a week over a period of ten weeks although Nasar (1998: 292) writes that it continued for less than this – six weeks – a total of 30 sessions in all – a fairly typical course. Six years before Nash's brain was systematically damaged in this way, work had already been published (Bourne, 1953) which pulled the evidence-based rug from under insulin shock therapy as an effective form of 'treatment' for 'schizophrenia', the supposed disease Nash was suffering from. It was in toto 'flimsy' (Bentall, 2009: 40). A Medical Research Council-funded randomised controlled trial in 1957 confirmed this (cited in Moncrieff, 2008: 34). One of the products of shock therapy – whether induced by insulin or electricity – is memory impairment. Nash did not escape these consequences and later attributed his 'inability to concentrate and to remember mathematics ... to [the] shock treatments' he received (Nasar, 1998: 19). Like others assaulted in this way, Nash 'resented it' and looked on it as a form of 'torture' (ibid: 292). Even prior to his own encounters with the mental health system he had a strong dislike of psychiatrists as did several of his mathematical colleagues. His first-hand experience of the best psychiatry has to offer did nothing to change this. He also regarded the other patients as 'more intelligent and more interesting than the doctors' (ibid: 256). It is also of note too, that during one of his periods in hospital (MacLean) the institution refused to permit anyone on its list of forbidden visitors to come and see him. Nash's belief in conspiracies was supposed to be delusional – no doubt things such as this added fuel to the fire. Given this background it is nothing short of incredible that Howard's film has the audacity to have the fictional Nash say to his wife that perhaps the psychiatrist (Rosen) is right and he (Nash) should 'think about going back into the hospital again'. This could be considered wishful thinking at best, but at worst and more likely it is outright deception and a travesty of the truth. Nash's own autobiographical statement (Nash, 2007: 10) leaves no room for doubt that his stays in psychiatric hospitals were 'always on an involuntary basis' and which his wife Alicia came to regret as a 'mistake' [which] 'had no beneficial effects, rather the opposite' (Nasar, 1998: 340).

Writing in *Psychiatry Online*, Ben Green (2007) describes the film as 'reasonably realistic' and maintains Howard carefully researched it, taking advice from leading psychiatrists in order to avoid the 'errors that typically litter other directors' work on mental illness'. Despite this assertion however Howard's film is littered with inaccuracies and not just those concerning the details of Nash's life (almost all the characters

A Beautiful Mind | 53

in the film happen to be fictitious which might be justified in providing a simpler but still largely truthful narrative). Besides the spurious claim made by Rosen at a family dinner that 'schizophrenia is degenerative'[14] there are the more serious and frequent factual discrepancies present in the film concerning the exaggerated claims made for the efficacy of psychiatric drugs. When Nash for example is seen failing to take his medication, a matter of seconds later we see his hallucinations returning. The unmistakeable implication being that the little pink pills eliminate hallucinations and delusions as effectively as an aspirin removes a headache and they are necessary to prevent any 'relapse'. But this is far from the truth. Firstly it might be more accurate to explain the supposed 'efficacy' of the major tranquillising drugs as being based not on the elimination of hallucinations and delusions but on the state of indifference that they induce in anyone taking them, so that they are less bothered by them (Noyes & Kolb, 1958; Moncrieff, 2008; Bentall, 2009). Then there is the difficult matter to explain that in developing countries where there are fewer psychiatric services both 'relapse' and 'recovery' rates are much more favourable than in the over-psychiatrised developed world (Bhugra, 2006). As the film draws to its conclusion we see a much older Nash, near the time of his Nobel award, informing a colleague that he takes 'the newer medications'. Nash, as was well known, ceased taking psychiatric drugs almost a quarter century before this and even then in his own words 'emerged from irrational thinking without medicine' (Nasar, 1998: 353). 'Most of the time', he says, 'I didn't take the medicine' (Nash, 2007). Realism here, as it so often does when the core beliefs of orthodox psychiatry are defended, like Nash's desk in the first half of the film, went straight out the window. Goldsman defended this on the spurious grounds that 'it would be dangerous' to suggest that 'people who are living in this state ... should stop taking their medication'. Howard, who in the commentary to the scene appears to be more concerned by the actors' makeup than in the liberties he is taking with the facts, remarked that it 'was so important to us to not represent the idea that you could be cured not taking your medication ... we felt that was the responsible thing to do'. One wonders in these sparse justifications, for just who would it be dangerous to suggest psychiatric drugs are not required to survive a nervous breakdown – human beings or 'Big Pharma'?[15] Similarly who is Howard being 'responsible' to? Certainly not the generations of needlessly drugged victims of a rampant biologically oriented, drug-obsessed profession that in all actuality has done very little to benefit those who are in the receipt

---

14. It is of interest that in response to this the fictional Nash responds, 'It's a problem that's all it is.'
15. See Mosher (1998) and http://www.moshersoteria.com

of its services. Howard and Goldsman – whose mother is a practising mental health professional (Mira Rothenberg,[16] a clinical psychologist) – do not for one moment contemplate that what might be far more dangerous than informing people of the limitations of psychiatry is a slavish adherence to a set of scientifically discredited 'truths' – an adherence which they so thoughtlessly exemplify. Back to Green (2007). In his brief evaluation of the film he writes 'Nash eventually complies with treatment although the main hallucinations never quite leave him. Nevertheless the antipsychotics do enable him to function, teach and have insight into what is real and what is not. *Without that there would be no film*' (italics mine). The film is therefore premised on a lie, a gigantic one at that. The nature of Nash's problems is misrepresented, as is the 'treatment' he received in and out of hospital. These misrepresentations are of such a systematic kind as to constitute a vehicle and an influential one at that for promulgating psychiatric propaganda.

Whilst the reason for some of the inaccuracies in the film can be laid firmly at the door of the book on which the film is based – Nasar's biography of Nash for example makes it quite clear in the opening pages that she wholeheartedly endorses the models of biological psychiatry, which she takes to be established fact. She believes Nash had a genetic predisposition to 'schizophrenia', a condition which she writes has 'mysterious' origins, was 'first described in 1806' (Nasar, 1998: 17), was 'defined for the first time in 1896' (ibid: 18) and labelled as 'schizophrenia in 1908' (ibid: 17) – a 'disease' which she holds is 'still widely regarded as a dementing and degenerative disease' (ibid: 21). She would do well to realise that a diagnosis is not a disease (Szasz, 2007b) and nor for that matter are hopes or fears. It is evident from careful reading of both text and endnotes that although Nasar has consulted psychiatric opinion throughout, this is without exception from a mainstream perspective – no dissenting or critical views are mentioned at all. Whilst there is much in the book to provide an alternative point of view on the reasons underlying Nash's psychological difficulties this appears to have been too subtle for the filmmakers to digest, who have instead opted to portray a story of a congenital madman who happens to be a genius and is then saved by love.

Concluding comments

No doubt the 'wonderful screenplay', to quote Ron Howard, helps to keep the dollars rolling in but it also shapes the sociopolitical culture and does so in a manner which is unlikely to benefit those who turn to

---

16. She is the author of *Children with Emerald Eyes* (Rothenberg, 2003). In an interesting foreword to this book, Peter Levine speaks of the 'over-medicalization of human suffering' (ibid: xi), something that Goldsman and Howard's work appears to endorse.

psychological or psychiatric services for help. John Forbes Nash has been transformed into a hero in the mould of all American heroes. Goldsman and Howard have made of Nash 'a connected cool person' and in so doing have fulfilled what they believed to be Nash's delusion. In presenting him as mad they have demonstrated his sanity. The 'merciless superego' on display belongs not to John Nash, maybe not even to Howard, but to a larger entity – the country. With their *objet d'art* both he and Goldsman have invoked the animus of 1950s America and have sought to reawaken the heroic dreams from that time and did so at a time when the Project for a New American Century was in full bloom. Looked at in this way the temporal contiguity of their film with the events of 9/11 is not accidental. The film is one aspect of the dream of American power – the death of countless thousands around the world is the reality. Nash's supposed insanity was a product of his time. In part he recovered because that time has now passed. The key dramatic themes of *A Beautiful Mind* belong within the grand historical narrative that we label as the Cold War – given a peculiarly American slant through McCarthyism. In locating the bizarre beliefs of the time inside Nash's head, and nowhere else, nationalist currents inside Hollywood may produce a thoroughly modern memory of that time, stripped of the everyday angst that permeated the fabric of social life back then. America no longer rules the world, even though it so desires. This is a desire that can never be openly admitted, as projected on to its opponents in some shape or form, it is the continuing rationale for war. The cinematic mind of John Nash is therefore a proxy for the cold calculating 'insane' mind of America and its junior partner in crime, Great Britain. *A Beautiful Mind* as a vision of the life of John Forbes Nash Jr. may shape future collective remembering of the man, his mind and his work. But beyond this, in so far as it turns the spotlight on 1950s America and the function of psychiatry in that period it is almost an empty vessel. Stripped of the emotional accuracy, critical reflection and historical menace (for our time) that characterised *Shutter Island* it is profoundly disappointing. Nash remarked that 'the ideas I had about supernatural beings came to me the same way my mathematical ideas did. So I took them seriously' (Nasar, 1998: 11). This film[17] as fantasy does not deserve the same fate.

---

17. *A Beautiful Mind* was listed in *Premiere* magazine as one of the 20 most overrated films of all time. http://www.screenhead.com/reviews/the-20-most-overrated-films-of-all-time/

Chapter Five

An Angel at My Table: Madness, identity and fiction

I remember one instance of a letter written to my sister June where I was actually quoting from Virginia Woolf, in describing the gorse as having a 'peanut-buttery smell'. This description was questioned by the doctor who read the letter, and judged to be an example of my 'schizophrenia'. For I was now officially suffering from schizophrenia, although I had had no conversation with the doctors or tests.

Janet Frame (2010: 253)

So many things go to make up a life and more still the life which is remembered. The collection of significant and not so significant circumstances that, woven together, signal to others and ourselves who we are and what the purpose and meaning of our life is are never wholly determined in advance, nor fully understood and agreed upon by those who play a part in the dramas which unfold. This assumes a peculiar importance when those who are in a position to fashion a narrative about us are both more powerful than we are and reliant on an impoverished set of 'facts' as to how we have come to find ourselves on a stage whereupon such people have been granted our story-telling rights. Society's major institutions – the family, the education, health care, legal and administrative systems – and our rights of passage through them at different times and places are instrumental in shaping who we come to be. In one sense they can be said to constrain the range of narrative possibilities awaiting us. It is also true that one's circumstances can brutally restrict and even dictate the identities we are permitted to assume or aspire to. In Janet Frame's case we are fortunate enough to have at our disposal both an intimate self-penned and a cinematic interpretation of the life she lived. From it we learn much more than how a 'freckle-faced, frizzy-haired little girl', one of the 'dirty and poor' children' (Frame, 2010: 43) of her environs ascended from the depths of the Great Depression in New Zealand to become recognised as one of the century's great writers. The path she took meandered through familial and local landscapes imbued with loss, hardship and the community of natural life around her, depositing her en route in a series of mental institutions for eight years. Like other recognised outstanding artists her story is a shining example of the limitations of the prevailing dominant outlook on 'mental health'. High-wire walker Philippe Petit whose wondrous traverse of the twin towers of the World Trade Centre in 1974[1] earned him a psychiatric interview provides one of many others. Petit succeeded in his outlandish and highly improbable quest as did Janet Frame in hers – a singularly chosen desire to become a great writer – but why should one have to achieve outlandish success to be embraced by society and enjoy the right to pop one's head into the clouds or spend the 'afternoons in treetops' (Petit, 2002: 6)? To scale such lofty heights of achievement almost requires that one casts aside the rules and regulations which structure and govern the lives of others, and opt instead for a path – a more challenging and rewarding one – which feeds rather than depletes our capacity to dream.

The current voices of reason and authority in our society stand in the way of such career choices. Foremost amongst them is the discipline of psychiatry, which as an enterprise seems premised on a corresponding wish to destroy all idiosyncrasies of thought whether grandiose or mundane (Roberts, 2010). The apparent relationship between creativity and madness which has occupied countless pages in books and journals (e.g. Ludwig, 1995; Vidal-Barrantes, 2004) can be explained not on the basis of any inherent vulnerability in those of artistic temperament but as a simple artefact of the outlawing of creative modes of thought – obliquely referred to in academic discourse as 'cognitive disinhibition'. There is probably no finer illustration of this than Salvador Dali's famous quip that 'the only difference between a madman and myself is that I am not mad' (Dali, 2007: 17). Dali gained worldwide recognition and notoriety for his ability, as well as developing a love of money (Buñuel, 1994) – and so he is sane. With cognitive *inhibition* thus the desirable norm, there has been a generalised retreat from trying to understand the human condition in terms of 'people's inner worlds' which of course is difficult and time consuming. A perusal of almost any textbook of cognitive psychology may suffice to make the point. So conspicuous by its absence from these volumes is the subject matter of our dreams, the exemplar of cognitive disinhibition, that an inspection of their dull dry contents would lead one to conclude that the human organism never sleeps. Dreaming, however unlike our waking cognitions, is not so amenable to manipulation, although efforts have been made[2] – ergo our lack of interest in dreams beyond their role as possible targets to be eliminated through selective REM sleep deprivation. We have arrived at a position where instead of any reflexive examination of who we are, what we may become or what

---

1. Petit's walk is chronicled in the documentary film *Man on Wire* (2008) directed by James Marsh.
2. The film *Inception* (2010) directed by Christopher Nolan provides an interesting example of how the military–industrial mind sees the issue.

we may create, we are now 'more interested in ourselves as neurochemical beings'. This is a result of the deliberate misrepresentation of psychiatric 'knowledge' and the consequent uncritical acceptance of claims made in it. A further factor is our fear of independent thought. Thus we prefer 'more superficial, glib, easy-fit narratives as ways of understanding ourselves' (Thomas, cited in Walsh, 2007) than getting down to hard work.

Jane Campion's film closely follows the narrative structure of Frame's (2010) autobiography, originally published in three volumes; *To the Island*, *An Angel at My Table* and *The Envoy from Mirror City*. Unlike other cinematic tales of true lives scarred by psychiatric good intent, Campion's is unusual in the extent to which it remains faithful to its original subject matter. It exhibits a fearlessness of the past and the lessons that might be drawn from it (Berger, 1972) and because of this she permits Frame to speak directly to the audience in a straightforward and appealing manner – and therein can be found its relevance to their lives. Frame's childhood is reconstructed and our own evoked as its events are recreated through a combination of the raw associative power of childhood rhymes, poems and stories. This is blended with a matter-of-fact depiction of emotionally salient episodes that move through Frame's development as a coherent visual and auditory ensemble, punctuated by the rhythms of absent memory as much as by what is recalled and retold.

We venture initially into the landscapes of childhood, and once there become privy to the mysterious world seen through a young Janet (Jean) Frame's eyes; to witness again the inexplicable and contingent cruelties against which one must do battle, its harshness, both intentional and accidental, is delivered through the incarnations of parents, teachers, brothers, sisters, friends, neighbours, strangers, animals and acts of God. It is a world of games, fun, learning, change, mourning and loss; a strange and familiar terrain which, despite its temporal binds to another era, is one which we can recognise as the one we have fought through on our road to the present day. What is apparent from the succession of set pieces which command our attention is not some assured knowledge of what sense the young Janet Frame would have made of it all, nor what a suitable interpretation of her life could be from a child's vantage point. What does emerge is a sense of the sheer complexity of living and its promise to exert untold effects upon those caught in the midst of its spell. Campion's 'simple' masterpiece educates us back into the 'ways of seeing' (Berger, 1972) and appreciating a life which, though it is perhaps more prevalent in the finer arts, has been successfully drummed out of too many who have passed under the hallowed arches which signal entry into the community of behavioural scientists. It shows us Frame's life in the manner of a phenomenological essay – 'a way of seeing which comes before words, and can never be quite covered by them' (Berger, 1972: 7).

Her life is thus presented and not judged, and hence is returned to the realm of mystery from which it sprang.

The relevance of this mode of presentation to our current concerns relates directly to psychiatric theorising and the presumptions upon which it is based. These are enunciated in the *Diagnostic and Statistical Manual of Mental Disorders* (DSM) (APA, 1994) and maintain that a so-called 'clinically significant' pattern of behavioural or psychological responses, in order that it be deemed a 'mental disorder', must not be an 'expectable and culturally sanctioned response' to events. Leaving aside the not unimportant issue that 'clinically significant ' remains an undefined term – at the beck and call of only the psychiatrically enlightened – this of course implies that every possible pattern of 'expectable and culturally sanctioned' responses to life's contingencies – including their cumulative and weighted effects – are known and can be specified in advance. This however is simply not the case and nor could it be. We do not know how people 'ought ' to respond given the practically limitless ways in which they can experience distress and trauma. By the time Janet Frame consented to admission to Dunedin Hospital – she was incidentally not aware that she was being admitted to a *psychiatric* ward – she had already experienced the deaths of her grandmother and grandfather, her sister Myrtle, and several beloved pets. In addition to this she had been publically outed as a 'thief' in primary school; been forcefully estranged (by her parents) from her close friend and confidante Poppy; faced numerous consequences of her brother's epilepsy, discovered literary and adult deceit, and suffered a variety of deeply embarrassing and humiliating public episodes. These related to her menstruation and her parents' inability or refusal to buy sanitary towels for her (just one aspect of the family's relentless poverty). Other significant events included the growing feeling of 'not being able to talk about life at home' (Frame, 2010: 116) and whilst still in her teenage years there was the fearsome outbreak of World War II, which 'haunted and confused' her (ibid: 214). This brief catalogue of some of the major episodes in her life which predate her encounters with the mental health system illustrates the problem. Psychiatry presumes that such a litany of unpleasant and taxing events could in principle be fed into a computer whose programmed rules (as specified in a perfect realisation of the DSM) would then reveal what the appropriate and culturally expected responses to these events are. It requires little foresight, merely honesty and an awareness of the complexities of human life to recognise that this is nonsense. The psychiatric gaze presupposes itself to be all-knowing and objective, simultaneously the view from nowhere and the view from everywhere, including the mind's eye of its subject – if it is to recognise the intentionality of its subject at all, which usually it does not. The directional gaze of Campion's film camera in contrast, is less grandiose in its claims, eschewing objectivity for a view of its subject which remains external though mindful of the unknown and weighty influences which bear down upon the person of Janet Frame. Through Campion's eyes, Frame's journey from the 'kingdom by the sea' (ibid: 135) to Seacliff, a somewhat different kingdom – a hospital 'where the loonies went' (ibid: 224) – becomes, whilst not predictable, certainly comprehensible. Frame's eternal question of 'why was the world?' (ibid: 40) would find no discernible answer there. The tortured souls in her company were bathed neither in poetry nor divine light.

What Janet Frame might have deduced from her initial contact with the mental health system is that honesty can be perilous if aligned to one's psychological struggles. Paradoxically, whilst her autobiography cemented her status as a truly great writer, it was an early foray in the genre, prompted by a university essay – written to meet the requirements of a psychology course – that led her into hot water. In an exploratory piece praised for its 'natural' tone and the evidence it provided of her 'real talent for writing' – she had dared to disclose the prosaic details of an earlier suicide attempt – an episode of swallowing Aspro by the bucketful. This written account terminated the secret contract she had with herself to never disclose the matter-of-fact loneliness and unhappiness with which she had been wrestling. Though later elated to have failed, and resolute that she would 'never again choose to kill' (ibid: 222) herself, the written confessional was seized upon by one of her lecturers, John Forrest, who together with other university staff read it as an invitation to visit her home and suggest a period of 'rest' at Dunedin Hospital. Shy, timid, unsuspecting of what lay in store for her, she consented. Her understanding of the significance of her own inner demons was limited to a presumption of their possible worth – a psychological badge denoting membership in the club of true poets, they of unquiet though renowned mind – and the secured attention of others, something which she craved but lacked the know-how to obtain by being her usual self.

Her identity as a psychiatric patient proceeded along its designated path despite an initial verdict at the hospital which proclaimed there was 'nothing wrong' (ibid: 224) with her. Honesty delivered its second painful lesson, when after three weeks her mother arrived to pick her up and take her home. Frame did not want to go and let her mother know this loudly and clearly. This was an act considered sufficient to cancel her imminent freedom and have her removed to the psychiatric kingdom by the sea, where her erstwhile troubles of the mind would bring her face to face with those who society has charged to police our thoughts. Her inauguration into the rituals of psychiatric barbarity thus began in earnest.

It was now 1945, World War II had come to an end (at least in the eyes of its victors), Janet Frame, at twenty-one, had come of age. With a prized published article in *The Listener* under her belt she had abandoned her fledging career as a school teacher, the constant fear of official judgement being the proximate cause, only to find herself now subject to the judgement of men more powerful than school inspectors. Their decision was that she was unsuited to free living. And so a prolonged psychiatric career beckoned – the 'wheel on [her] wagon' (ibid: 77) well and truly broken.

Campion narrates the shock of entering this bleak and horrific environment with few words – letting the images tell their own disjointed story – as Frame is physically and emotionally engulfed by the merry-go-round of wayward and intellectually disabled adults[3] inhabiting her new living space. 'A world I'd never known among people whose existences I never thought possible ... a concentrated course in the horrors of insanity and the dwelling place of those judged insane' she would later write (ibid: 227). On her return home she announces, anxious and perplexed to her family, 'I've got schizophrenia!' The response, from her sister Isabel, of 'What's that?' is one which would be hard to imagine today – from anyone, now that the entire populace has been so thoroughly immersed in the rampant hearsay world of biological psychiatric categories and claims. Yet sixty-five years after Frame's dramatic dining room entrance, there are still no tests for the reputedly mysterious condition and no one appears any more able to say what exactly it is supposed to be – save those critics of the profession who argue that it has no existence at all beyond its status as a social construct manufactured and distributed by psychiatrists! What this situation does indicate is that the advances in knowledge which appear routinely in physical medicine are notable by their absence in its psychological counterpart (Bentall, 2009). On looking up the putative condition of schizophrenia in a book Frame's sister dutifully pronounces it to be 'a gradual deterioration of the mind with no cure', an apt metaphorical description perhaps for the state of the psychiatric intellect, which withers with each new edition of the DSM. Toward the end of the twentieth century clinical psychologist Mary Boyle (1990) pronounced schizophrenia to be a 'scientific delusion'. Psychiatry as ever took no notice of its critics.

Dunedin Hospital was the first stop in Frame's long tour of New Zealand's psychiatric facilities, taking in Seacliff, Sunnyside and Avondale mental hospitals. One is struck by the endlessly cheerful names of these institutions – sun, sea and dales – perhaps evolutionary psychology's paradise lost, which at the very least conjure up images of holiday resorts

---

3. At the time depicted in the film most people with Down's syndrome were institutionalized. Most died in infancy or early adult life whilst still in hospital.

and at most promise miraculous recovery of lost innocence. Six weeks in Seacliff, after another brief respite at home, led in turn to Sunnyside on the recommendation of John Forrest's friend, a 'Mrs R'. Frame had sought her out in the hope of having someone accompany her to the dental department of the local hospital to deal with her decaying teeth. The visit to Mrs R resulted in counsel to seek psychiatric treatment. 'They have a new treatment there,' she remarks, 'which appears to be successful.' The new treatment was ECT, and as we can imagine, it was not at all helpful.

Cinematic treatments of shock therapy are interesting on a number of accounts. They are usually portrayed with convincing realism (see also for example *A Beautiful Mind, Changeling* and *One Flew Over the Cuckoo's Nest* which are discussed in this volume). The realism to hand in these representations is an exceedingly brutal one. One almost reels from the stench of institutional antiseptic as Janet Frame is plugged into the mains to thereby have her brains 'fried'. In a room replete with screaming people – others being administered the same treatment – she is held down by nurses as her body convulses and arches in waves of response to the medical assault upon it. These scenes do far more than convey a realistic impression of what ECT entails, they also strip away the scientific modernist pretensions of physical 'therapy' in psychiatry. As with the non-developments in the 'science' of 'schizophrenia', so with the 'science' of ECT. Beyond cosmetic flourishes in the design of electrical equipment and the use of anaesthetic and muscle relaxants[4] prior to the procedure, effectively nothing has changed with respect to either the mode of delivery of electroconvulsive therapy or the rationale behind it – from 1945, when Frame got her 'volts from the blue', to today.

On screen we are not overtly instructed to judge these proceedings but in the truthful way in which it is presented we are certainly extended a tacit invitation to do so. These are interventions normally carried out behind closed doors away from the public's prying eyes, in places where the sun doesn't shine, where no peaceful waves lap against the shores of the mind and the only thing green may be the staff uniform. The numerous medical documentaries and medical soaps over the years which have induced a state of acquiescence to medical genius in one TV audience after another have tended to give this sort of stuff a wide berth. And for good reason, the evident barbarity would expose not only the lie that jolting the human brain with electric power in the name of controlling and treating people constitutes benign intervention – it would likely, through its common imaginal store with the electric chair and the Frankenstein myth, also expose psychiatry to accusations of charlatanism and soul murder. Of course if ECT really were so beneficial and safe, we would no

---

4. This is referred to as modified ECT.

doubt by now have had a retinue of salesmen flogging us self-improvement kits, so that we might plug ourselves into the national grid and achieve our own personal electrical ecstasy.

Shortly after we see Frame being given ECT, the camera moves to a corridor in which several women on their hands and knees are seen scrubbing the hospital floors. To the right, occupying a full half of the screen is a large wastebasket. Over this we hear the calm voice of Kerry Fox, who plays Janet Frame, informing us that 'over the next eight years', she 'received over 200 applications of electric shock treatment, each one equivalent in fear to an execution'. Campion's intentions are unmistakeable. In juxtaposing elements of women's subjugation (cleaning floors, a subservient posture) with both a repository for dirty linen and a verbal rendition of psychiatry's mishandling of Frame's solitary and, for a time, unhappy character, she is rejecting at a stroke psychiatry's bogus claims for scientific respectability and technological progression in its 'treatment' of the 'mentally ill'. These signs of oppression, she is arguing, have no place outside the dustbin of history. Sadly they continue to infiltrate the present.

In Frame's own country women still comprise the majority (66%) of those given ECT (NZHIS, 2002) – a similar proportion to that found in other 'enlightened' countries (Read, 2004b). Frame's memory, in her own words was 'shredded' by the treatment, 'in some aspects weakened permanently or destroyed' (Frame, 2010: 266), her life 'thrown out of focus' (ibid: 252), sentiments which constitute nothing new or extraordinary in the testimonies of people administered shock treatment. Ernest Hemmingway committed suicide soon after he had it. 'What is the sense of ruining my head and erasing my memory, which is my capital, and putting me out of business?' he asked (cited in Read, 2004b: 90). No sense indeed, but the psychiatric authorities have continued to deny that systematic memory loss is a predictable consequence of ECT. Hemingway departed this earthly paradise after he had it, Frame stayed behind to soldier on.

Frame may have doubted she had it – but real mental strength must have been required to endure the squalor and deprivatisation of the self which informed the etiquette of her hospital life and in the midst of her psychiatric career, the further loss of another sister, Isabel who drowned whilst on holiday with her mother. Stripped of dignity, privacy and agency, she became hopeless, adopting a state of 'physical and emotional submission' (Frame, 2010: 267) to her 'custodial capture' (ibid: 262). She survived, probably for two reasons, only one of which the film does or can make clear. Confined to one of the hospital back wards, one of the 'forgotten people' (ibid: 262) of institutional psychiatry and indeed society, and seemingly destined to remain there for life, Frame experienced the joys of publication; her first book – a collection of short stories entitled *The Lagoon* –

was brought to her with obvious delight by her sister and brother-in-law. And so her dreams of being a writer were kept alive whilst she existed on the minimum of psychological life-support. For this work, she went on to win the Hubert Church Memorial Award for best prose, one of New Zealand's most prestigious prizes. The fact of this alone was enough to see the hospital cancel the leucotomy[5] they had scheduled for her.

Prior to this act of literary escapology we see Frame being told that 'there's no need' for her 'to be frightened', that the operation 'will do you the world of good'. With the new-found fame of the award however, the question of 'what's best' for Frame suddenly mutated in the eyes of the psychiatric authorities. Their goal now, was not to hack into her brain, but to build up her confidence and strength and get her home. The consent of her mother who had 'signed the papers' for the operation somehow paled into insignificance beside the greater authority of the watchful eyes of the nation and its attendant representatives – the steely members of the press who had first announced the news of the award.

That the choice of treatment for a patient was seemingly dependent, not on the scientific worth of the treatment, but on public opinion may seem highly unusual, but in many ways this is disturbingly typical of the way psychiatry operates. In the absence of any valid tests for 'mental illness' opinion is all that counts. Frame, unaware that this is the norm, appears perplexed that her diagnosis and treatment were arrived at without any formal tests or that the 'experts' who oversaw her 'case' over a period of eight years spoke to her in toto 'for about 80 minutes' (ibid: 263) – an average of 10 minutes per year. However, a pseudo-medical system, in which individuals' responses to the slings and arrows of outrageous fortune are seen as nothing more than the signs of a malfunctioning machine, has no primary interest in listening to anyone trying to make sense of the world. As for the 'entrances' and 'exits' of putative mental disorders on the stage of agreed mental disorders: schizophrenia, homosexuality, kleptomania, oppositional defiant disorder, PTSD, ADHD etc., and now the latest of them all, *at risk of psychosis syndrome,* these are *all* arrived at by a voting procedure, a matter of professional politics not scientific legitimacy (Szasz, 2007b). Professional titles, publishing justifications of the status quo in in-house journals, wearing white coats, having the power to dispense drugs and brain surgery and using Latin-sounding names to classify people's undesirable behaviour may give the appearance of scientific credentials but what makes for real science goes beyond the aesthetics of representation.

Equally important to Frame however amongst the factors that

---

5. Leucotomy refers to the cutting of white neural fibres connecting the frontal lobe of the brain with other brain regions. Lobotomy is a modified form of the procedure (El Hai, 2005). The terms are often used interchangeably.

propelled her back to hope was her furious desire to lend a voice to her incarcerated companions, spurred by their sadness and courage in the face of adversity and inhumanity. She singles out the humanity of her fellow inmates and some of the nursing staff, but for those who wield the true power in psychiatric establishments, the staff 'who wrote the reports and influenced the treatment' (Frame, 2010: 263) she has nothing but contempt. The illusion of medical interventions for bona fide medical disorders does not survive an account in which certain 'treatments' were 'threatened as punishment for failure to co-operate' where 'not co-operate' might mean a refusal to obey an order, say go to the doorless lavatories with six others and urinate in public while suffering verbal abuse' (ibid: 263). Frame's treatment like all who are transported through the mental health system is ultimately about pleasing other people – those who have authority – and who wish to see compliance with 'normality', which effectively means giving up wild ideas, such as being a writer or excelling in some way. For many of us, a society where intellectual or artistic endeavour is derided whilst it is in fact secretly envied entails a painful reminder of our own shortcomings or past failings – yet another reason why many artists are the bane of the status quo. Why appearing to be indistinct and like 'everyone else' should be regarded as a model of good functioning in a culture which is supposed to pride itself on individualism has never been satisfactorily explained. Perhaps like much today, what we are led to believe about the world and why it is as it is, is simply a lie.

Friends of Frame and others in the institution who were unlucky enough not to win a major prize or be in the running for winning one found themselves in the fearful queue for neurosurgery. The results of the failed medical experiments performed on them are amply displayed in the film's images of dishevelled, bandaged and broken people being escorted through the hospital grounds. They resemble nothing so much as battle-scarred soldiers, meandering through a prisoner of war camp. Now with a measure of fame, she received the rubber stamp of approval by the state and after the requisite time outside the hospital walls was declared officially sane.

Always a traveller since her childhood and now a free woman, Janet Frame began a long voyage to rediscover the delights and struggles of personal autonomy and the conviviality of other writers and artists. In travels abroad to England, France and Spain she developed her writing, and her social and sexual selves. When her natural magic-realist imagination and 'why was the world' questions as companions, her journey was one that was as much through her own consciousness as through the far-flung corners of humanity and the world. Frame brought back a wealth of prose forging new links between herself and the world, but never succeeded in consigning the painful past to a distant shore within the ebb and flow of her own memory. 'The evil that men do lives after them' Shakespeare's Mark Antony once said; so too the misguided machinations of mental health professionals. The consequences of Frame's prior identity as a 'schizophrenic mental patient' never left her – either on a practical or personal level. When on a visit to London she found herself excluded from a career in nursing because of her 'mental history'[6] she endeavoured to learn the 'truth' of her past and sought out an appointment and voluntary admission to the Institute of Psychiatry.

The 'learned' doctors after a period of several weeks' observation, interviews and tests eventually pronounced that she had 'never suffered from schizophrenia' (ibid: 446) as if it was possible to know many years later whether one had earlier contracted a type of 'illness' for which there has never been any physical signs or valid diagnostic tests.[7] A more logical conclusion to be reached by the Institute's great and good, after due consideration of all available information, might have been a confession that it is impossible for anyone to suffer from schizophrenia as there is no evidence whatsoever that any such condition exists or ever has existed. As this was not forthcoming her earlier schizophrenia was thereby recast into the realms of an unfortunate 'misdiagnosis'.

Beguiled by the attention and warmth lavished upon her during her stay at Europe's premier centre of psychiatry and struck by the stark contrast with how she had been treated in New Zealand's, Frame was taken in – not just by the linguistic trick of misdiagnosis. The version of psychiatry in the 'home country', as England was to New Zealanders, seemed to be a more 'real' and authentic variety in comparison to the sham and cruel operation in her home country. Frame was not just hoodwinked by imperial majesty and psychiatry's language games however, she was also deeply confused by the decision, as by then her 'certain' knowledge of her 'schizophrenia' had woven itself into the fabric of her personality and had become intrinsic to her identity. She had learnt to wear it like an old coat, to negotiate awkward social encounters and to possess something which would act as a measure of the damage done to her and why. Though she doubted whether she had really suffered from the condition, it had become 'the answer to all [her] misgivings' (ibid: 455) about herself. The loss of legitimacy to this identity came as a shock. She felt she had been left with nothing. 'At first the truth seemed more terrifying than the lie. How could I now ask for help when there was nothing wrong with me?' she lamented. The answer supplied by the good doctors was that the problems she had 'been experiencing were a direct result of all those years ... spent in hospital'. These problems included

---

6. 'How could you possibly think of being a nurse? It's out of the question.'
7. A point Szasz has made whilst giving evidence in a court of law (see Szasz, 2007c).

especially an internalised lack of responsibility, stemming both from the mistaken nature of the illness metaphor and the institutional restrictions and punishments for the exercise of volition. Rare as 'patient' perspectives are in the academic literature, such consequences have rarely been the subject of research, another forgotten aspect of the discipline's secret history.

Reality continued to present a mirror image to the version she had constructed from her experience of it, when one of her London psychiatrists, a psychotherapeutically minded Dr (Robert Hugh) Cawley, somewhat different from his namesake from *Shutter Island*, positively encouraged her not only to write about her experiences in New Zealand, but to do so in a manner consistent with her temperament. 'If anyone tells you to get out and mix and you don't want to ... don't!' Cawley added to this advice the suggestion that she support herself temporarily on National Assistance.[8] The result of this guidance and encouragement and Frame's talent was a body of work in which the lives of the misfits, non-conformists and troubled people of the world – those readily processed by the alienist toward conformity or oblivion – are the centre of attention – none more so than her second novel *Faces in the Water*[9] (Frame, 2009) which gives us the story of Istina Mavet,[10] from her point of view. It is a strongly autobiographical and graphic portrayal of the 'overt sadism' and 'pervasive stupidity' (Mantel, 2009: ix) of mental hospital life, a chronicle of depersonalisation, 'humiliation and fear' (ibid: x), where protest is outlawed and 'weeping is a crime' (Frame, 2009: 9). Frame considered the truth she told in it had been softened, 'subdued' (Frame, 2010: 463), deliberately so, in order she said to make it more believable. Too little of this truth has changed since Frame's psychiatric sojourn and too much of it has been forgotten. Though she exorcised many of the psychiatric demons through her writing, its traumatising effects were never entirely banished. She grappled perennially with passivity and compliance learnt from her hospital days whilst memories of the destroyed human beings subjected to brain surgery stayed with her throughout the remainder of her life – haunted continuously by the shell of a life that might have been hers. 'The nightmares of my time in hospital persist in sleep and often I wake in dread, having dreamed that the nurses are coming to "take me for treatment' (Frame, 2010: 267).

---

8. At the time a form of Social Security payment for unemployed, injured or aged people.

9. Written around the same time as Ken Kesey's *One Flew Over the Cuckoo's Nest*.

10. Her name is an amalgam of 'truth' (from the Bosnian, Serbian, Croation language) and 'death' (from the Hebrew; Mantel, 2009: vii). Radovan Karadzic, the Bosnian Serb psychiatrist indicted for genocide and other war crimes, might constitute a variant name on the themes of 'lies' and 'death'.

Concluding comments

The childhood dream of Janet Frame to be a writer bore fruit, tinged with the bitter kernel of oppression. Campion's film, an essay organised around what is for Frame the perennial existential issue of 'what it is to be a human being' tells the story of how she planted the seeds, nurtured their development and overcame the harsh elements in her path. There was no inevitability to her success, no rules or master plan to chart the way to genius, only a chaotic path wandered with a singular lofty goal in mind. Perhaps this is the trail taken by many more people than we can imagine, with the ill-fated wayfarers delivered to normality and lost dreams or served up as psychiatric cannon fodder. One wonders what literature Frame might have produced in a society tolerant of difference and ecstatic about the exquisite possibilities of imagination – a society without fear of experience and lacking the affront of psychiatry. Campion considered Frame to be an 'intensely sane' (Campion, 2010: xii) woman. Yet rather than self-examination, psychiatrists still pass their time dreaming up diagnoses for her – although she is now deceased – a paradigmatic exercise in the pursuit of the absurd. In love with the written word, Janet Frame was an admirer of Yeats, whose lyric touch in *Meditations in Time of Civil War* (Yeats, 1982: 230) contains some of the soul searching the purported science of mental health desperately needs.

> *We had fed the heart on fantasies,*
> *The heart's grown brutal from the fare,*
> *More substance in our enmities*
> *Than in our love.*

Chapter Six

One Flew Over the Cuckoo's Nest: Insanity, justice and control

The white people told only one side. Told it to please themselves. Told much that is not true. Only his own best deeds, only the worst deeds of the Indians, has the white man told.

Yellow Wolf (cited in Brown, 1991: 316)

In the introduction to Ken Kesey's classic novel, Robert Faggen (2002) advanced the view that psychiatry, by the end of the 1950s, had already reached the height of its prestige in the American imagination. Basing his position on the challenges to psychiatric legitimacy posed by Szasz, Laing, Foucault and Goffman, Faggen would have us believe that the transition to the swinging sixties bookmarked the 'failure' of government 'to use science and technology to control the world' (Faggen, 2002: xiii). In the aftermath of this scientific letdown – psychiatry being the presumed source of it – Kesey began the work for which he is most well known and which provided the means for Milos Forman to launch the most scathing attack on the institution of psychiatry in the history of the big screen.

While the CIA-sponsored experiments of the day with their legions of hallucinogenic drugs failed to deliver the anticipated levels of population control which had been their hope, it would be a profound mistake to conclude that the ending of these research programmes signalled the end of government-driven and psychiatrically organised dystopian dreams – for which read our nightmares. While *Shutter Island* tracked the birth of these programmes from the wreckage of World War II, *One Flew Over the Cuckoo's Nest* deals with the next stage in their development. The new strategy that would take centre stage in the psychological management of the world signalled a retreat from manipulating the creative powers of mind and memory, to a position involving their wholesale subjugation. If opening up the mind through experience could not deliver a compliant population, then the new technologies of psychiatric control emerging in the 1950s and 60s would propose that its closure could deliver the desired ends just as effectively. So 'successful' have the chemical and physical restraints employed thereafter been in shutting down the mind that they have been with us ever since. The story of Irish-American Randle Patrick

McMurphy tells us much about the nature of the criteria used to evaluate this success.

McMurphy swaggers into the hospital as the archetypal runaway from the straightjackets of conformity. He has been transferred from a penal work farm where his unruly behaviour has been judged the product of a 'psychopath' (Kesey, 2002: 13), though the possibility that he has been 'feigning psychosis to escape the drudgery of work' (ibid: 42) there has not been entirely overlooked. The book and the film chart his passage[1] through the institutional labyrinth that is run by 'Big Nurse' Ratched, former army nurse and incumbent corporeal representative on the ward – the stronghold – of the inhuman 'Combine'. From behind her big 'glass case' (ibid: 30) on the ward, she exudes her quiet love of power and to the accompaniment of her cold rehearsed expressions dispenses medication to the 'troops' as if from a military bunker. McMurphy is not alone in his journey however. As a traveller through the bleak landscape of psychiatric 'care', he is joined by Chief Bromden, the Native American narrator of the novel.

The Chief begins his account of McMurphy's odyssey with an anticipation of our own disbelief. What he has to tell us we might find 'too horrible to have really happened', 'too awful to be the truth'. 'But,' he continues, 'it's the truth even if it didn't happen' (ibid: 8). Faggen's reading of the text, whilst otherwise engaging and enlightening, misses the simple significance of this. In feigning the role of a deaf and dumb mute, Bromden may be, as proposed by Faggen, a trickster, but nonetheless his statement is no invocation of the 'essential trick of art, a lie that tells the truth' (Faggen, 2002: xv). As a 'Vanishing American' (ibid: xv) in a psychiatric facility he is doubly aware of the ease with which the truth is apt to disappear when what one has to say speaks to the abuses perpetrated by the powerful – on the one hand by White people to Native Americans and on the other by psychiatric staff to inmates/patients. As Marx, 1852/2006: 15) was apt to remind us 'the tradition of all dead generations weighs like a nightmare upon the brain of the living' and in the contemporary United States, the extinction of Native American tradition is a living nightmare. Bromden knows this, though neither Faggen nor the psychiatric authorities of *Cuckoo's Nest* give us any indication that they do.

No wonder Bromden is silent, 'big as a dam mountain' (Kesey, 2002: 187) he may appear, but cut down to size by the lies, ignorance and killing power of the White man, he has seen the land of his people stolen, treaties dishonoured, people massacred. A Native American might find

---

1. Following Goffman (1961), we might say that what is under the microscope here is McMurphy's career as an inpatient.

justification in this for not wishing to share the contents of his own thoughts – which are all he has left to protect. Dispossessed of all else by the White 'men', Steve Biko's truth that 'the most potent weapon of the oppressor [is] ... the mind of the oppressed' (Steve Biko, cited in Mngxitama, Alexander & Gibson, 2008: 70) speaks to Bromden's plight. The Native past stolen, Bromden's silence is an attempt, however misguided, to ring-fence his mind. The evidence of his reason then is to the White man evidence of his irrationality, his silence read as an 'illness' they cannot understand. Yellow Wolf's lament, which opens this chapter, echoes round the antiseptic white walls and sinks of the asylum. Here the history of the American West repeats itself. Bromden's reaction to this history awaits McMurphy's spirited intervention before it can make the leap from tragedy to farce.[2] Until that moment silence is resistance.

Faggen is guilty of mystification – he proclaims the lie, without bothering to tell us exactly what it is – though in doing so he invites accusations of denial by implying Bromden's unmasking of our denial of psychiatric and colonist brutality is something not wholly true. He is no doubt afflicted by the modern White Man's Burden – enunciated by Zizek (2010: xii) as 'the lived lie' – 'the 'spontaneous' state of our daily lives ... which requires a continuous struggle' to free oneself from it. To embark on this quest for Zizek necessitates a suitable state of terror of oneself. Thus only once we have allowed ourselves to become suitably terrified do we have the psychological necessities to confront the 'undesirable truth' and the terror of psychiatry. If that can be looked in the eye without blinking then perhaps only the Buddha lies in wait on the road ahead. And we know what we must do with him.

In the novel, it is the Chief who introduces us to the workings of the 'Combine', the abstract mechanised entity which permeates the fabric of his reality, structuring, moulding, stimulating and directing the totality of human existence to fulfil its brutal soulless purpose. The hospital is one part of this remorseless, manipulative monstrosity, where dissidents, straying from its grand design and in need of servicing, are sent to be 'fixed', by drugs, or in cases of more severe violations of its unconscious code to the 'brain murdering room' (Kesey, 2002: 15) where the medical fraternity dispense electroshock or lobotomy to bring the wayward into line. Through the Chief's eyes Kesey anticipates the underlying revelation of *The Matrix*. The Combine, like the Matrix, 'is everywhere ... all around us ... you can see it when you look out your window or when you turn on your television. You can feel it when you go to work, when you pay your taxes.' It is 'the world that has been pulled over your eyes, to blind you

2. Prior to his death, Will Sampson, who played Chief Bromden, bemoaned the portrayal of Native Americans. 'Hollywood writers and directors are still using 'em for livestock,' he said. 'They somehow just can't seem to bring it around to give the truth about Indians.'

from the truth' (Wachowski & Wachowski, 1999). The response of Keanu Reeves's kung fu fighting, gun-toting character in the Wachowski brothers' work moreover bears more than a passing resemblance to McMurphy's own – neither believes that the rules of society apply to them. Reeves' Neo is instructed by his master 'Morpheus' that the rules 'can be bent'. McMurphy gives the impression that they can be disregarded. In this, as we come to learn, he is profoundly mistaken.

From our modern sensibility, this machine-like system may be recognised as the global corporate colossus now strangling the planet and hurtling human civilisation to destruction (Bakan, 2005).[3] Buñuel (1994: 18) saw in the 'technological progress' it brought, the exile of 'morality and spirit to a far distant territory'. The absence of Native American morality and spirit in the film, with the concomitant removal of Bromden as the central figure of the narration[4] signals a further silencing of the Native voice – a directorial act of psychosurgery – on one whose delusional thoughts of 1963 can now be heralded as far-sighted perceptiveness of the dangers lying in store. Then as now the damage wrought constitutes a mere externality on the balance sheet of the corporate behemoth. The narrative perspective is now provided by Forman's camera which centres its attention squarely upon McMurphy, whose on-screen introduction to Chief Bromden via a barrage of fake Indian hollering, is sadly out of place in the film and unworthy of an otherwise great work of art. It could be argued that through this device the director shows McMurphy's relatively 'uncontrolled nature' is not altogether desirable (Slater, 2008: 127). This may, however, be reading too much into what may simply have been a cinematic ploy enacted by the filmmakers, to get the audience to identify with McMurphy, that is he must first be shown to be prone to the same kind of everyday idiocy as was presumed to exist in the minds of 1970s theatregoers. The favoured stereotype of the old-style Hollywood Western, which was unable to grant the Indian even the status of 'noble savage', these racist shenanigans were absent from the novel[5] and are also out of character with McMurphy's otherwise respectful interactions with the Chief.

The film begins with a sweep across the moody, brooding landscape of the world outside the hospital, a wild natural world which follows its own rhythm. Tracking Nurse Ratched's lone drive to the hospital, her entrance through the locked gates of the ward introduces us to the rigid

---

3. Indeed the RAND Corporation – which figured in the preceding discussion of the life of John Nash – could also be interpreted as comprising a major component of the unseen Leviathan.

4. Kesey terminated his creative involvement with the film because of this.

5. McMurphy's character in the novel however does refer to the Black orderlies using racist terms.

unnatural hierarchy of the hospital-cum-prison. White Female nurses instruct Black orderlies in their duties – 'they are in contact on a high-voltage wavelength of hate' (Kesey, 2002: 28), who in turn exercise their slice of authority over patients, distinguished by their relative status as either an 'acute'[6] or 'chronic'.[7] Behind the scenes and set to appear some eight minutes into the film are the order of psychiatrists; the great chain of being from the mighty to the lowly, reproduced in a psychiatric theory down the ages which has equated the 'patients'' allotted place on the bottom rung of the sociological ladder with some biological mark of Caine. Faggen is right to note the undue visibility of middle management – with the real power seemingly hidden. The 'nightmare of middle management' (Faggen, 2002: xvii) on the ward however is that this is an expression of psychiatric power – bequeathed to it by the state; the nursing staff and orderlies who dispense the medication and wear the jailhouse keys are its subordinate agents, taking their orders from Big Pharma and Big Psychiatry.

When we applaud the 'realism' of hospital life in Milos Forman's film, what we are noticing in fact is reality. Filmed in Oregon State (mental) Hospital, many of the background participants were actual patients in the hospital granted their celluloid immortality on the say-so of the institution's superintendent Dr Dean Brookes who thought it might be therapeutic. While not challenging Brookes' sincerity in any way, that a cameo role in an Oscar-winning movie can be considered part of the therapeutic armament to be deployed against an array of supposedly inherited biological dysfunctions only serves to illustrate how absurd the medical model actually is. Perhaps the National Health Service (NHS) might wish for this to be considered in the next NICE guidelines.[8] Brookes himself makes more than a passing (and convincing) appearance as the principal psychiatrist in the hospital, Dr Spivey[9] and to be fair to Brookes he was by all accounts a tolerant and decent man in his dealings with patients. His views about drug treatment, however, are not typical of his profession – he preferred not to use them. 'After all,' he is reported to have said, 'how could we know who and what they are if we had them on drugs.' His first appearance with Nicholson on screen was completely improvised, with Brookes' only instruction being to interview 'McMurphy' as if he really were a new admission. This makes the exchange all the more absorbing and telling.

6. 'Sick enough to be fixed' (Kesey, 2002: 13).

7. 'Not in the hospital to get fixed, but just to keep them from walking around the streets giving the product a bad name' (Kesey, 2002: 14).

8. NICE refers to the National Institute for Health and Clinical Excellence, the body in the UK which makes recommendations to the NHS on new and existing medicines, treatments and procedures.

9. None of the psychiatrists in the film were played by actors. All worked in this capacity at the hospital.

Brookes/Spivey explains to McMurphy that he has been sent to the hospital by the prison authorities because he has 'been belligerent, talked when unauthorised ... been resentful in attitude toward work in general, that [he's] lazy'. Following Nicholson/McMurphy's scathing retort, 'Chewing gum in class,' the psychiatrist elaborates, 'You've been sent here because they wanted you to be evaluated to determine whether or not you're mentally ill.' Were Brookes/Spivey not a member of a thoroughly dishonourable profession the only thing to do at this point would be to show Mr McMurphy the way out. Belligerence, resentment toward work, laziness, or talking when others don't like it are not and could never be, in any bona fide scientific sense, medical conditions, though there have been no shortage of psychiatrists over the years who are unaware of this – as any survey of the psychiatric literature will confirm. McMurphy is next invited to comment on why the prison authorities might think he is mentally ill. The invitation itself demonstrates how far the psychiatric tentacles now extend in society. Just as in many spheres of life today where administrators and bureaucrats routinely 'diagnose' anything from 'dyslexia' to 'depression' – all considered as grounds for circumventing the normal requirements of organisational performance (in a higher education establishment for example for work to be handed in on time) which can be waived in exchange for membership in the club of the mentally disordered, lifelong membership granted – nobody bats an eyelid at the implied suggestion that prison warders may be adept at spotting allegedly complex medical conditions.

From McMurphy's standpoint his detention stems from his proclivity to 'fight and fuck too much' – he has five arrests for assault on his record. 'What can you tell me about that?' Brookes/Spivey asks and the inextricable and arbitrary nature of the social rather than biological norms which fashion the diktats of 'psychological' medicine are laid bare in Nicholson/McMurphy's dazzling reply, 'Five fights huh – Rocky Marciano's got forty and he's a millionaire.' 'That's true,' admits the psychiatrist and what else could he do but admit it – for there's socially rewarded and approved fighting – as in sport, and as carried out by members of the various armed forces on behalf of the state and greater corporate empire and then there's socially disapproved fighting. McMurphy's behaviour obviously falls into the latter category – the only one for which genetic and physicochemical explanations have ever been sought. This tells us something about the values which dominate psychiatric 'science', values which have no reasonable place in a truly scientific community. It is not 'evidence-based' but 'eminence-based medicine' (de Vries, no date). Accordingly until such time as psychiatric 'knowledge' is firmly expunged from the scientific canon, any claims as to the superior wisdom of the institutions of modern scientific reason (e.g.

Dawkins, 2006), are demonstrably flawed and lack both credibility and conviction.

McMurphy's (and our) initiation into the customs and practices of the asylum continues with his participation in the compulsory group therapy sessions run by the Big Nurse. Here is the collection of miscreants whose lives will intertwine with McMurphy's and spin off in a multitude of unexpected and poignant directions. These are the hapless and very different individuals on whom Big Nurse exercises her intense repressed power: Harding, Billy Bibbit, Martini, Turkle, Bancini, Sefelt, Taber and Cheswick. One of the beauties of the film is that whilst none of these characters are central to the issues playing out in this story – each in their own way plays a pivotal role in revealing both Nicholson's character and the truth of the hospital – the inhuman nature and purpose of the psychiatric system. They are the visible raw materials for reprocessing and remodelling which the hospital undertakes to fulfil its function within the larger system of control.

Through the guise of the group therapy sessions we become immersed in the workings of what Goffman (1961) referred to as the total institution. Ostensibly organised to permit each person to 'talk ... discuss and confess' (Kesey, 2002: 40) their way to psychological nirvana, the pseudo-democracy of the 'encounter' group realises a system of surveillance and control. Here the men's activities are scrutinised for compliance with the staff's wishes, under the requisite condition that their 'carefully worked-out schedule' of activities in the hospital space must not be disrupted. The psychiatric 'knights of reason and order' have abandoned their accredited mission to elevate the anxious, confused and despairing to the heights of super-sanity and have settled instead for lowly compliance with their own social norms. Masquerading as beneficial for personal readjustment, the *raison d'être* of the asylum is to maintain itself. As a result the patients must defer to the hospital staff and submit to the routines of the institution. They are told when to work, what to do, what not to do, when to play, what to say, what not to say, when to smoke, when to sleep. All this is deemed to be 'therapeutic' and appropriate for their 'adaptation' into society. They are deemed incapable of making the simplest decisions about their own lives. Robbed of adulthood in perpetuity, outside relationships are also constrained, under the eternal watchful gaze of paternal authority. This infantilisation of the psychiatric patient continues to this day, denied the fundamental liberties of control over their own body and person and trust in their own reason, motives and desires. All these rules McMurphy has come to challenge. He is no psychotherapist, no worker of unconscious or 'subconscious miracles' (ibid: 53). He brings with him the dream of liberation, to reawaken the weary and the watched from their slumber, to drag them 'out of the fog' (ibid: 112) and away from the path to existential and spiritual destruction.

McMurphy's need to live fully and exuberantly and haul the men from their stupor of submissiveness means confronting the deadening inflexibility and obsession with control that pervades everything from the orchestrated 'medication time' to the thickness of the hospital air. The simmering feud with Nurse Ratched is raised a few notches higher once McMurphy, referring to Big Nurse's own justification for the 'therapeutic community' meetings, expresses his personal desire to 'get things off his chest'. The cathartic opportunity duly granted, he proposes changing the usual ward routine so that the men can watch the opening game on TV of the World Series baseball game. Ratched, unhappy at any attempt to change the 'carefully worked out schedule', provokes McMurphy's ire, expressed in his earthy rejoinder to 'fuck the schedule!' In what she now presumes is a skilful manoeuvre Ratched proposes a vote with the outcome to be decided by majority rule. Amidst a circle of timid and fearful faces McMurphy manages to elicit the support of only Taber and Cheswick. Nonplussed that no more raised hands are forthcoming, he appeals to their patriotism, and their masculinity which the pious Big Nurse has set her sights on eliminating. In McMurphy's eyes she is a 'ball-cutter'. 'What's the matter with you guys?' he pleads, 'I haven't missed the series in years, I watch [it] even when I'm in the cooler, they run it there or they'll have a riot.' There's no riot however as a smiling Ratched announces the feeble vote is 'not enough to change ward policy'.

The opening salvo has been fired. The second volley will soon sound, but not before McMurphy has given the men – and in particular Chief Bromden – an uncompromising lesson in the desperate necessity of freedom. It is the unstoppable force against the immovable object as the architect of rebellion pits his raw strength and desire against the 'dinky little gizmo' (ibid: 109) that is a half-ton marble fountain. McMurphy, power of nature that he is, does not prevail. But his mission – to hoist the contraption from the floor, carefully engineered fittings notwithstanding, and follow in the wake of its intended trajectory through the window onwards into town in order to watch the ball game – opens a mental doorway in those who witness it. 'But I tried, didn't I? Goddamn it! At least I did that,' he sighs. But his failure has stirred the sleeping tigers of self-determination; the next instalment of 'group therapy' will be different – in place of the favoured 'imbecilic normality' (Cooper, 1976: 150) of submission, the meetings will henceforth be stalked by the phantom of liberty.

As the 'veritable angel of mercy' (Kesey, 2002: 54) Nurse Ratched continues prosecuting her (and the system's) psychological war against the assembly of men. She encounters resistance, first from Cheswick who questions the 'therapeutic value' of interrogating the vulnerable Bibbit, and then argues for the therapeutic worth of watching the World Series. A second vote is instigated, which appears unanimous, with all the men raising their hands. The sham democracy of the ward is now revealed for what it is as a Margaret Thatcher-like Ratched rejects the vote, citing the lack of support from the nine chronic patients on the ward – the 'poor sons of bitches' who 'don't know what we're talking about!' intones McMurphy in astonishment. But despite an additional electoral winning vote solicited from the Chief, now making it 'ten to eight', Ratched refuses to countenance McMurphy's victory, let alone acknowledge that the final vote was cast in an act of self-assertion from a supposed 'catatonic' man. Livid, she announces the meeting adjourned and the vote closed. The regime of the ward – her order, the hospital order, the status quo – has been threatened, and no spontaneous act of human dignity, no resurrection from the psychiatric dead to life of any importance, can bring any joy to the heart of the Big Nurse compared to that – and she, in the words of Dr Spivey, 'one of the finest nurses we've got in this institution'.

McMurphy it is clear is no ordinary man; in Bromden's eyes he had never been still long enough for the Combine to imprint its dulling circuits into his flesh and blood. His maverick, working man's vitality, with its aesthetic of bawdiness, song, laughter and poker, is locked in a fight to the death against the unseen power that dictates the flow of reason on and beyond the ward, everything that lives within and without the mortal boundaries of Nurse Ratched, the influence that stole all the vibrancy from the soul of the little girl who grew to be the Big Nurse. That power stalks McMurphy, inviting him, tempting him as he waltzes and skirts with its awfulness in the Big Nurse's earthly form. McMurphy's Eros to Ratched's Thanatos, he is the reminder of what she has lost and must take back or destroy. To deaden the painful reminder of her own submission she will service the Combine and draw the life from all around her and turn it to stone. She is the embodiment of psychiatry as the art and science of petrification. Like its sister discipline psychology, psychiatry is premised on the idea of the individual, locked in a dance to death with the notion that a person's entire history lies stored in the internal neurological and physicochemical cogs of their nervous system. Such a narrow view negates at a stroke any conceivable possibility that who we are can just as well be found in the ongoing nexus of relationships that connect the individual, conceived as a person of free will, with the attendant interacting physical, political, economic, professional, familial, religious, military and judicial spaces of human existence.

When trouble strikes in life – as it is wont to do – people invariably look to the bigger picture – the most superordinate framework they have – to resolve the contrariness and apparent senselessness of their misery. Or at least they did before biological psychiatry colonised the inner spaces and devoured the available interpretative repertoires of personhood. Poetry, song, dance and laughter – McMurphy's gifts and primary weapons against the stultifying world of the hospital – have always figured large in such repertoires. In the triumphalist, 'no-nonsense' permitted, epoch of Big Psychiatry allied to Big Pharma, these have become dangerous adversaries to the degraded rationalism on offer – though perhaps it might be more accurate to refer to this form of rationalism as one 'imposed'. To elaborate one's life with these arcane abilities risks incurring the wrath of those who service the monster of the mental health system and who, knowing nothing of the virtuosities of prose, read incomprehensibility as an invitation to physical restraint (permanent or temporary). In *One Flew Over the Cuckoo's Nest* McMurphy is the antithesis of all that the sterile asexual asylum stands for – and what we observe is essentially an existential contest between them. Rogue and small time con-man though he is McMurphy's tricks inspire resistance and self-belief in the deflated human beings around him and for this his ruses betoken no moral failing. They signal rather an inversion of the accepted moral hierarchy in the hospital. This is exemplified by McMurphy's imaginary reinvention of the World Series game on TV once the door on the democratic will to watch it has been slammed shut by Ratched. He conjures up an exhilarating and fantastic ball-by-ball[10] commentary on the game faced with nothing more than an inert blank screen. This becomes the tabula rasa for McMurphy's resistant imagination. For the first time, genuine merriment, excitement and delight reverberate through the ward as the men are drawn to the screen like bees to a honeypot. A homily to the creative power of the mind, illuminated by the light of a thousand laughs McMurphy celebrates the 'imaginary other' and simultaneously rescues it from the pathologising anti-imagination of psychiatry. One battle has been won. More lie ahead.

Throughout the proceedings McMurphy's presence subverts many of the assumptions which surround the mental health system – both in regard to its workings and those who enter it for processing. This however is no designated exercise in destigmatising 'mental illness' or, as Slater (2008) argues, of inverting the roles of sanity and madness across the staff–patient divide; rather it is one of questioning its entire reality as well as the nature of the 'treatment' dispensed to psychiatric service users. When McMurphy hijacks the bus taking the men on a fishing trip the characters play on the meaning of being crazy, make fun of being 'nuts',

---

10. Producer Michael Douglas described this as 'the most brilliant piece of acting I've seen in a long time'. Nicholson researched the World Series game of 1963 and provided his own account of it from his memory of the batting order and what each player did.

even representing themselves as doctors from the hospital – effectively demonstrating both the inability of outsiders to distinguish them from their medical masters and the interchangeability of identities across different role positions. *Cuckoo's Nest* as such effectively rejects a psychological analysis of the hospital inhabitants' mental state in favour of a sociological analysis of their status. As McMurphy himself later says to the men, 'What do you think you are, for Christ's sake, crazy or something? Well, you're not. You're not! You're no crazier than the average asshole walking around on the streets.' This is an observation and interpretation which Ratched is able to acknowledge as 'challenging' though without questioning the system of power which enables her to have McMurphy, an obviously sane man, committed against his will, and denied his liberty for more time than specified in his original sentence, even when Dr Spivey favours sending him back to the work farm. Spivey aside, who doesn't 'see any evidence of mental illness at all', the predominant view amongst the other psychiatrists is that McMurphy is 'dangerous', though 'not crazy', not 'overly psychotic' whatever that means! So it is his apparent dangerousness which points the way to his downfall. But in what way can McMurphy be considered an actual danger to them? This is not spelt out, though one may readily surmise that it is his *view* of the world which is the prima facie threat, his 'disregard' for their 'discipline and authority' (Kesey, 2002: 134) and that what is concretely threatened by it is the psychiatric profession's unquestioned rights to drug and detain people against their will; its compulsion to impose standards of normality on everybody else and exercise the denial of life, liberty and fun under the guise of health care.[11]

Ultimately much of psychiatry is predicated on defining otherness and dissent as firstly unacceptable and secondly as illness, particularly when the unacceptability in question is that which stimulates ethnocentric discomfort. At issue in *Cuckoo's Nest* and in the wider world is the centrality of the Anglo-Saxon perspective in not just defining 'normal' behaviour but offering it up for definition in the first place. Fernando (2003: 6) has described the collusion of psychiatric power with 'race power' as a 'deadly mixture'. Little wonder therefore that so much confusion surrounds the concept of dangerousness – that prediction of who is and who is not dangerous are prone to massive error (Fernando, Ndegwa & Wilson, 1998) and often based on nothing more than a person's physical size, perceived physical strength and of course skin colour

---

11. As an interesting aside – some years back whilst teaching a university course in 'Abnormal Psychology' in which I presented a critical perspective of the prevailing medical model, one of the students who had regularly met with me to discuss the issues which arose from the course, confessed to me that his mother – a psychiatrist – considered me to be a 'dangerous person'.

(Littlewood & Lipsedge, 1997). It is surely no accident that the two principal characters compulsorily detained – Chief Bromden, a Native American, and McMurphy, a working-class Irish American – have developed their views of the world outside of the strictures of WASP (White, Anglo-Saxon Protestant) society. Their somewhat different cultural standards and traditions do not line up with the imposed norms of the DSM nor produce the desired ethnocentric comfort in those who have sworn an oath to the psychiatric 'bible' and the power enshrined within it. Unfortunately even amongst the more culturally sensitive of psychiatrists there appears a marked tendency to restrict the concept of culture to 'exotic' ethnic groups with white people of all nationalities and social classes presumed to live in a ubiquitous monoculture – the one from which their own history originates. One could be forgiven for noting how psychiatrists have thereby assumed the position of supreme judges and overseers of the mono-ethnic white culture they see around them. No matter how hard are the attempts to suppress them, the roots of supremacist thinking that lie at the heart of psychiatric ideology – once clearly visible in the 1930s – keep pushing up through the dirt.

While McMurphy's catalytic presence reanimates the *élan vital* of the hospital inmates, it also raises the defensive shield of the threatened authorities, drawing their fire to him like a magnet. His martyrdom, his recognised 'sacrifice' in giving life to others in exchange for an existential death that will at first slowly and then rapidly engulf him, extinguishing once and for all his own life force bears more than a passing resemblance to Christ's. Indeed McMurphy, seen by the Chief as a 'giant come out of the sky to save us from the Combine' (Kesey, 2002: 231), makes of his new accomplices true fishermen, before he returns them to the bosom of the hospital family changed men, awakened by the inner light (of the sacred heart). And like Christ it is they who ultimately give him up to the Big Nurse, the ECT machine and finally the scalpel. McMurphy's 'Christ' though is neither devilish nor divine, merely a stumbling, incarnate representative of the ecstasies of life. Only Chief Bromden, who sees the bigger picture, who McMurphy has lured back to the speaking world, tries to warn him – sees the dogged mechanical persistence of authority 'working on him'. McMurphy too senses this, feels it grinding him down, knows he is cornered and must escape, but he has been late to realise the dangers of playing the mental health system for his own advantage and in allowing himself to fight the Big Nurse on behalf of the men at no risk to them. Thus he does not go willing to his fate. But his drunken sleepy failure to make good his moment of opportunity, having secured the keys to freedom during the overnight revelry he has brought to the ward, means he must bear witness to the desperate suicide of Billy Bibbit, prompted by the sadistic promise of the Big Nurse to make known to his mother everything about Billy's sexual liaison with Candy, a friend of McMurphy's invited along to his farewell party. McMurphy's subsequent unfettered attack on the Big Nurse, in which he unsuccessfully tries to squeeze the life out of her – somewhat more rapidly and literally than her own metaphoric attempts to squeeze it little by little from her charges – paradoxically, reveals him to be, not the sociopath of the colourless psychiatric cookbook, but a sociophile. He is injured by the needless death of a man who along with the Chief he had been nurturing back to independence and autonomy in a manner utterly foreign to the so-called healing arts of the alienist.

But is there also mileage in a theological reading of McMurphy's fate as illustrative of the perils of unthinkingly abandoning oneself to the irresistible temptations of freedom? After all, he gambles, fights, profanes and womanises in the true spirit of Bacchus. Perhaps, but only if it is also recognised that McMurphy's medicopsychiatric day of judgement comes at the hands of the same conservative forces of state and religion that did for Christ in the first instance, soured the fruits of liberation theology in the past century and would willingly throw away the key to both joy and knowledge in our own. Milos Forman recognises these same conservative forces from his own past. 'This is a Czech movie,' he says, 'about a society I just lived [in for] twenty years of my life.' He proudly asserts, it is 'about everything I know'. And what he knows is life in a totalitarian Soviet satellite state. It is the 'Big Society', ruled by the cold fear of the state. It is one which has been growing in the shadows for some time, working as Reich (1974) understood to make 'little men' of us all. It is now, with the help of psychiatry, closing the doors on the open society and standing full-square opposed to the 'free critical thinking' and 'commitment to the truth' necessary to sustain it (Soros, 2010). It is no accident that as Nurse Ratched leaves the hospital premises and McMurphy inaugurates the temporary respite from tyranny with his midnight party, the television news playing in the background announces the possible opening of the Berlin Wall during the forthcoming Christmas period. The asylum, like the corporation, provides an essential working model of totalitarian rule, and psychiatric practice the pseudo-scientific vehicle for extending the rationality of this to the outside world. Like the isolated East German state which denied essential freedoms to its citizens, psychiatry stands isolated and estranged from its social and natural scientific neighbours. It is fluent in the lexicon of science but not its syntax, unable to produce or substantiate any compelling truths which by the right and proper application of research methods could justify its claims to epistemological authority. It is 'Junk Science' (Parks, 2000). The Berlin Wall closed again after the festive period of 1963. It was demolished barely a quarter of a century later. We can hope that the wall protecting the foundations of psychiatry from prying eyes also lives on borrowed time.

McMurphy's subsequent lobotomy is performed with the same punitive intent as the earlier sessions of ECT, delivered to control and caution against transgressing the suffocating normalities of psychiatric and social reason, the penalties all the more severe when the unsanctioned behaviour is anger, undisciplined laughter or incitement to autonomy. By underestimating the strength of his opponent, he has rendered himself unable to fight it effectively (Popper, 2002: x–xi). He cannot comprehend why trying to avoid work one minute sees him sent to a mental hospital and then once there is required to 'sit there like a goddamn vegetable' in order to demonstrate his sanity. The only logic to this is one of obedience. His cheerfulness, disdain, and single-minded courage cannot by themselves slay the psychiatric dragon. Turned into a zombie by the 'help' which Nurse Ratched believes in, McMurphy's days of wine and women are over – left 'meek as a lamb', an automaton whose days as a functionally competent human being are behind him.

With Billy's suicide and McMurphy's soul destroyed, it is left to the Chief, no longer inured to the clockwork operations of the Combine, to take up the challenge and restore our faith in the endless possibilities of freedom. Restored to his full size, as McMurphy has taught him, he hurls the fountain through the hospital windows and crosses the threshold dividing the imprisoned from the cool natural stillness of the free world. McMurphy is dead, his 'big hard body' has relinquished its 'tough grip on life' (Kesey, 2002: 278), smothered by the Chief in a necessary act not without love to deny the Big Nurse her trophy and free McMurphy and his memory from her icy grip. McMurphy's physical death at the hands of the Chief should not be confused with his prior existential death, coolly executed by the 'skilled' hands of medically trained staff. McMurphy's only remaining freedom is in his physical death. The Chief's lies in front of him.

Concluding comments

That such a film uncompromisingly critical of institutional psychiatry enjoyed such critical and commercial success[12] speaks not only to the considerable artistic merit of the film but also to the high regard with which its themes were recognised and endorsed by the public at large, not to say the actors and film crew. Jack Nicholson considers it one of his

---

12. The film won five Oscars, six Golden Globes and six Baftas and is recognised by the American Film Institute as one of the greatest films in the history of American cinema and as 'culturally, historically, or aesthetically significant' by the United States Library of Congress.

personal favourite performances and according to producer Michael Douglas it is 'probably the most important picture in every one of our résumés'. Surprisingly previous analysis (Faggen, 2002; Bloom, 2008) has avoided any examination of the role of organised psychiatry or the mental health system in the unfolding of events, opting instead for a careful analysis of the motives guiding the main protagonists, a preference for individual rationality over institutional rationality. I would argue that both are needed if the film and the book are to be fully understood.

One wonders several decades later, with the inroads into the public consciousness engineered by the pharmaceutical and psychiatric industries, not to mention the stream of lies which have poured from their rivers, whether such a film could be made today. At the time it was independently financed and made before any distribution deal was in place and it took great effort to persuade any hospital to allow them to film there. Nowadays its backers would have to contend with the same enemy McMurphy was fighting – but grown stronger. As we witness the erosion of democracy and see personal and corporate responsibility dissolve before our eyes we must not make McMurphy's mistake of underestimating this foe. His and our nemesis is not simply an individual, an organisational Big Nurse, but an entire corporate system juxtaposed with a widespread organised set of social representations and psychiatric newspeak which provide its psychological driving force. This is an opponent that finds its home in the minds of men and women as much as in the wide open spaces of the hospital, pharmacy, prison, courtroom or school, an enemy against whom neither brute force nor reason will suffice unaided. Our fear of the imagined (or actual) violence of other people, a paternalistic attitude toward the 'mentally ill' and an unfettered fear of responsibility all provide the perfect nesting conditions for the survival and growth of the psychiatric 'meme' in our minds.

In the making of the film the actors shadowed real patients in the hospital for one week, none being interested in analysing whatever 'mental illness' or medical problems they were supposed to have. The cast frequently remained 'in character' during the period of filming. This meant that it was on occasion not an easy task to separate illusion from reality. Whilst the actors sought to live inside the minds of disturbed people, Forman saw in the environment around them the real patients who were 'people ... desperately trying to look normal'. Its undoubted realism aside, the film and the novel on which it is based are works of fiction, but as depictions of institutional psychiatry and its hidden intent 'it's the truth even if it didn't happen'.

Chapter Seven

Spellbound: Psychiatric power, surrealism and truth

It is not necessary for the public to know whether I am joking or whether I am serious, just as it is not necessary for me to know it myself.

Salvador Dali (cited in Ballard, 1974)

This journey into one of the heartlands of psychiatric power – the image – began in *Shutter Island* with a battle for reality between a fledgling modernist psychiatry and an alleged fantasist and critic – whose ultimate socially sanctioned identity and existence would be decided by the outcome. In this final exposition we encounter another contest between fantasy and reality and examine psychiatry in its original and most enduring representational form – in the incarnation of psychoanalyst wielding the sword of truth in heroic defence of the patient's mind. At stake once more is identity and existence. *Spellbound*, loosely based on the novel *The House of Dr Edwardes*[1] was originally the brainchild of producer David O. Selznick. The mogul, influenced by his own experiences in therapy, wanted a vehicle to showcase psychoanalysis. Palmer and Saunders' gothic-flavoured original turned into something altogether different in the hands of screenwriter Ben Hecht and the master of suspense, director Alfred Hitchcock. The final film was the outcome of a conceptual battle between Selznick and Hitchcock which the latter did not always win. There is however enough of Hitchcock's trademark camera work, studied anxiety and concern with the unconscious to make this a quintessential Hitchcock work. The director, a man who loved to be misunderstood (Truffaut, 1985), set about creating a fragmented visual and psychological kaleidoscope set against a background of murder, fear and desire. Though unable to altogether escape the constraining hand of Selznick, Hitchcock's homage to psychoanalysis as detective work still manages to excite on a number of levels, not least because its narrative structure, somewhat self-referentially, possesses some of the thematic and temporal consistency of the dream sequence which forms the kernel of the story.

---

1. Written by John Palmer and Hilary Saunders (1927/2002) using the pen name of Francis Beeding.

As the film commences the opening titles inform us that this is a story about psychoanalysis, 'the method by which modern science treats the emotional problems of the sane'. Through this opening stance – more Selznick than Hitchcock – we see the reverence with which psychoanalysis was then embraced as part of the status quo. But what does this say about the 'insane'? No doubt they were to be found beyond the outer limits of this high society love affair with psychotherapy – beyond the domain of the wealthy worried well, and they had emotional problems that presumably were *not* to be treated by modern science. Thus in one deft move, a few words have relegated the mad once again to the status of 'unpeople' – whose fate will turn on their response to the out of sight, unmentioned tools of the trade.

For its public endorsement by Hollywood, psychiatry will be presented dealing with the 'normal' mad – not the 'mad' mad. The character played by handsome Hollywood heart-throb Gregory Peck most certainly belongs to the former category. Big cinema functions psychologically on audience identification – however fantastically – with the principal protagonists. Yes, 'audiences love to dip their toes into the cold water of fear' as Hitchcock remarked, but at the time *Spellbound* was produced the necessary identification with the fearful subject had yet to extend its reach into the terrifying enclave of the 'psychotic' let alone the 'psychotic' anti-hero. By the time Hitchcock had taken his camera to the Bates Motel fifteen years later however his interest was most definitely with the latter.

In *Spellbound* we have Viennese depth psychology as Western – psychoanalysis at the OK Corral – a *High Noon* confrontation between the forces of reason and repression unfolding not in the badlands of Dodge City but the temporal borderlands of World War II and the looming Cold War. The past actualities and future possibilities of mass violence haunt the era, and unable then as now to be fully assimilated either psychologically or socially they thus become fertile material for psychological defence. Enter Analysis – the beacon of the West to represent the forces of light – personified in the beautiful Dr Constance Petersen (Ingrid Bergman) confronting the dark forces of (Nazi/Eastern) repression[2] in the guise of the heir apparent to the directorship of Green Manors Mental Asylum, Dr Anthony Edwardes[3] (Gregory Peck). Edwardes, like Teddy Daniels over sixty years later, is not what (or even who) he seems. The stage is set for Analysis to be glorified as the ego ideal of the victorious West, the triumph of reason, while beyond any public

2. She must also contend with psychiatric colleagues trying to molest her, though this is glossed over as cheerful banter and horseplay.

3. With 'A' and 'E' for initials Edwardes comes across ultimately as both accident and emergency.

gaze or scrutiny an id/superego alliance prepares for Cold War (psychosurgery always lurks in the psychiatric undergrowth of the talking cure). In the true fashion of depth psychology this is supremely disguised – served up as romantic melodrama and film noir fronting a beginners' guide to psychoanalysis.

Edwardes is a man burdened with guilt, possessed of a secret known only to his subconscious. Petersen and her fellow analysts are tasked with peddling the talking cure in its purest form, to 'uncover and interpret' the 'complexes' which 'disturb' their patients,[4] but they are also salesmen and women peddling talking and listening as a branch of medicine. Those are simple democratic skills that should suffice to make doctors of us all – but democracy is on global life support in the 1940s and the hierarchical field of medicine enlightened or repressed can countenance no other masters. Conceptualised by the therapists as 'illnesses' and 'diseases', their clients' problems are absolved of any metaphorical allusions to ill health and are mistaken literally for the real thing and assigned labels nurtured through medical subterfuge and the new (in the US) psychobabble to masquerade as bone fide medical conditions. This unchecked scientific fantasy escaped the attentions of the moviegoers of the period as well as the screen analysts whose determined fight to uncover reality intentionally leaves their own professional daydreams and confusions of identity securely locked in the cellar of their and society's unconscious. But if we can thank analysis for one insight it is that reality usually leaks out from the most tightly locked of psychological secrets. In this directorial outing Hitchcock called on the services of Salvador Dali to illuminate the uncharted territories of the troubled psyche, but not even Dali's 'paranoiac-critical'[5] attitude could drive these surreal 'devils of unreason' from the placid psychiatric soul nor disturb the 'smug frozen face[s]' of the custodians which cover the essential lie within. Dali may however have left behind something for critics of our time to enjoy. Of the analysts' lack of reflexivity and Dali's contribution there will be more to say later.

On setting foot in the institute Edwardes is introduced as the author of a mighty tome – *Labyrinth of the Guilt Complex* – and before long his hesitant but penetrating gaze, accompanied by the soothing melodic strains of romantic violin,[6] has bonded with the animated and radiant eyes

---

4. We are given no indication as to whether the patients are voluntary or committed.

5. Dali's use of the term 'paranoia' refers to a 'delusion of interpretation' – a state which could be induced voluntarily to produce a set of perceptions which for the artist, though no one else, were internally consistent (Bracken, 1986). The paranoiac-critical method occurred to him after encountering Lacan's work (Martinez-Herrera, Alcantara & Garcia-Fernandez, 2003).

6. Described by Hitchcock as 'terrible', this piece of melodrama probably owes more to Selznick.

of the lovelorn Dr Petersen. As all seasoned writers since Shakespeare have known, the course of true love never runs smooth and so the emergent love is very soon confronted by an explosion of Edwardes' psychic turmoil. A simple gesture of Petersen's with a fork elicits the frozen signs of panic and a rash of anger to cover the deep stirrings of his own unconscious guilt.

Petersen, like everyone else in 1945, is at a crossroads, a woman established in an independent career who must pander to the desires of her male colleagues in order to substantiate their fantasy of feminine mystique. Hers is the predicament of many women emerging from gainful employment in the war economy and while we see the clinic in which she works as a veritable showcase of psychoanalytic folklore, the work conducted there presupposes the gendered power structure of the day. The psychotherapeutic professions have rarely attended to their own position in the hierarchical class-, race- and gender-powered structures which circumscribe the contours of normality (Smail, 2005) and so Petersen must grapple not only with the mysteries of the irrational mind but also the inequities of the established 'rational' one. A woman with some authority she may be but she is also recognized as an oddity, out of place with her stiff grey-suited bourgeois colleagues, and therefore like Edwardes an outsider. In the mode of Zizek we can at this juncture easily imagine a counterfactual development of the story in which Petersen rebels against her smug sexist colleagues, questions the absence of women amongst the psychiatric staff, punches the next lecherous analyst who tries to grope her and is subsequently pronounced psychotic. Deemed 'agitated' and 'unanalysable' – this being her own fault naturally – she is then rejected by the established order and sent for a brain operation to make her more malleable; psychoanalysis giving way to the harsher physical treatments required to warn others of the penalties for transgressing the codes of the symbolic and social order. Analysis is thereby an accommodation to this order, afraid to look at the unconscious where it is at its most chastening – in the realm of the social and historical.

Within the grounds of the clinic free-floating anxiety and guilt appear as the order of the day. The analysts' prescription to 'open the locked doors of the mind' through their talking and listening sessions is emphasised in the early moments of the film in a series of confessional set pieces in which patients parade before the camera, giving full vent to a variety of revelatory declarations. These are patients as psychoanalysis would wish them to be – obliging and conforming to type – witness the obligatory oedipal confession by one of them, Mr Garmes, who claims to have killed his father – deftly handled naturally by Petersen with a curt explanation as to the childhood origins of 'delusional' beliefs. The effect of her incantation in lightening Garmes' mood seems almost miraculous –

more hypnosis than psychoanalytic magic – as if only the spoken word of an analyst could convince poor Garmes that he hadn't killed his father. Doubtless other people must have told Garmes this for him to be in the hospital in the first place so we can only surmise that this 'scientific' discipline of psychoanalysis is truly amazing. Of course another possibility is that one might wish to believe anything Ingrid Bergman might say – but that would only be to confuse her motherly and subdued erotic magnetism with the benefits of years of self-analysis or beauty with truth. Related they might be, the same they are not. While this interaction signifies the incredible to contemporary viewers it does serve to highlight the immense expectations and power surrounding psychiatry at the time. This is a brand of psychotherapy dispensed with the ease and assurance of selling fog. And what the spectator is being sold along with instruction into the basic tenets of Freudian psychoanalysis is confirmation of their own ignorance and an assured belief in the charmed wisdom, rationality and expertise of psychiatrists and psychoanalysts. Despite her impressive curative abilities, as well as Garmes' meek demeanour, Petersen takes the view that he is 'agitated' and in urgent need of drugging 'for a few days'.

No wonder then that we subsequently learn Garmes has run amok, tried to kill one of the psychiatrists and in a fit of despair cut his own throat. Such a scenario, logically consistent with a client's fury and despair from such cavalier treatment, is wholly believable. In a real-world mental health setting however the 'aggression' and 'self-harm' would probably be read not as a professional wake-up call but as confirmation of deep psychiatric 'insights' and the object lesson to be drawn from the unfortunate experience would be to ensure that in future the Garmeses of this world be given enough drugs to fell an elephant. Beyond the notion of transference or accepting praise for those of their clientele who go some way toward putting their life in order, psychiatrists rarely figure as agents whose actions play a prominent role in determining or directing the course of their clients' behaviour. Responsibility is invariably split. It is not they who are responsible for undesirable outcomes. That is, the bad is expunged as the complete responsibility of the other and, once located there, can then be attributed to the influence of a psychiatric disorder – a disordered personality or treatment-resistant 'disease'. So it is in psychiatry that the notion of disorder/mental illness functions, as Lacan would have it, as the threatening 'big other'.

As the apparently benign swiftly gives way to the pharmaceutically malign, one is reminded of Zizek's (1992: 161) radical riposte to our customary interpretation of the divine: 'good' he writes, is merely 'the mask of radical, absolute evil', the mark of an 'indecent obsession'. This 'indecent obsession' has been well understood by generations of people whose unhappy fate has been decided at the hands of those who have been on a mission to propagate their idea of the good (Todorov, 2003). 'The greatest harm to the human race has been done by poets,' Petersen whimsically confides to Edwardes, but this is not so. This is an escape from reality. The 'war on terror', the 'war on drugs', and the everlasting 'war on mental illness' are also attempts to escape from reality or at least to bend it so out of shape that one hardly notices. In the process however these endeavours to do good, like all wars, have brought untold and incalculable misery. The doting psychiatric lovebirds know nothing of this, and seem to live in a parallel universe from the one ravaged by world war. As early twenty-first century spectators we cannot but succumb to a double nostalgia as we watch the story shuffle along against its idyllic backdrop of hope and possibility – firstly for the simplicity and goodness of the imagined past evoked by the whimsical noir spectacle of the 1940s and secondly for an imagined psychiatry working in the interests of the patient alone against the oppressive forces of society – here represented by the police and the infidels who shun the great leap forward that is psychoanalysis. This is now the stuff of our libertarian dreams, one residing in the structure of a wish no less fantastic than Dali's theatrically staged excursions into the territory of nightmares.

As the couple drift into an imagined haven of new-found love, Edwardes' psychological vulnerabilities resurface, triggered once more by specific patterns of visual stimuli. Petersen grows suspicious when she discovers a discrepancy between Edwardes' signature in his famed book and the handwritten note from the newly arrived man delivered to her. Now suspecting that Edwardes is not who he claims to be she confronts him and for the second time in a day is faced with a man who claims he is a murderer, albeit one with no idea of who he is. Whoever thought psychoanalysis could be so exciting? 'How can a man lose his memory, his name, everything he has ever known and still talk like this, as if he were quite sane?' Peck asks. Peck is no 1940s Matt Damon,[7] though this is a penetrating question, and one that cinematic treatments of amnesia continually shy away from. But there is an interesting parallel concerning amnesia at work – psychiatry too has lost its memory – and from around this time and yet it continues to 'function' in an integral manner as if it were quite a 'normal' profession. So perhaps Peck could interrogate his analytic brethren as to how they keep the facade in place. 'Are you afraid of me?' he continues. Faced with a man who claims he has amnesia and is a murderer, Petersen's calmly delivered negative reply – delivered with the cool repose of a female Clint Eastwood – could serve as an object lesson to any mental health professional. We know little of Constance

---

7. According to the advertising for the Bourne series of films, 'Matt Damon is "Jason Bourne", another amnesic man with an invented identity'.

Petersen's background but the tranquillity of her response, given the customary professional resort to drugs and restraints when faced with the merest whiff of dangerousness, suggests the wisdom of a Zen master, that she has fearlessly cultivated the 'art of fighting without fighting' to a level Bruce Lee would have been proud of. Her Buddhist variant of psychoanalysis could no doubt fill volumes – to be summarily described in the paradoxical logic of Zen as psychiatry without psychiatry!

Inspired by her faith in her new-found love, in her capacity to enjoin reason and emotion in dynamic harmony, Dr Petersen turns detective, giving an object lesson to her male colleagues in the virtues of marrying intuition to rationality. In moving effortlessly between the roles of sleuth and analyst Petersen follows a tradition which can be traced back to Freud (Zizek, 1992)[8] – not a comparison however which has gone down well with everyone in the profession. Gabbard and Gabbard (1999) for example extol the arcane technicalities of psychoanalysis and psychiatry in contrast to the prosaic fundamentals of police work. Whatever the respective merits of these differing positions, a good many people do now see psychoanalysis as having fundamentally more in common with detective work than biological medicine – both seek to understand behaviour from the standpoint of motives, both utilise clues to look beyond the given towards some deeper reality, and both rely on establishing a degree of trust and rapport with those who provide them with vital information.

As the police appear on the scene and begin piecing together the facts surrounding the disappearance of the real Dr Edwardes – now presumed dead – it is apparent that in *Spellbound* we have stumbled upon a psychological circus, a grand theatre of the postmodern self in which the leading players walk the high wire of ambiguous identity. The story dovetails through a merry-go-round of characters, each with varying claims as to who and what they (and others) are. Murchison, the retiring head of the clinic, announces himself as an analyst to be 'a man of science'; he asserts that the impostor Edwardes not only has amnesia but is a murderer and 'paranoid' – but it is in fact he who is later revealed as the chief villain, whose crime has been committed on the back of his own psychological disintegration and personal failings. Other analysts confidently declare that the fake Edwardes is a 'criminal' and an 'obvious suicide' waiting to happen.

Meanwhile Petersen encases herself like a Russian doll inside successive layers of identity as first she assumes the mantle of detective, and from within that feigns to be both a teacher and a married woman. These are the creations of her encounter with a hotel house detective who, not content with his ordinary job title, sees himself as a 'kind of

---

8. Hitchcock further extols the virtues of the psychiatrist-as-detective in *Psycho*.

psychologist' – again intertwining the nature of police and analytic work. Finally there is Peck's character – a 'dangerous madman' in the eyes of the police, alone of all these players who professes he does not know who he is – perhaps the most honest statement that any of these characters make on the subject of who they are! Goffman's thesis on the theatrical presentation of self is accordingly writ large and lends weight to constructionist narratives which proclaim the death of the self. We are the author of our own selves – but in the place reserved for the real self there is no one. We may all have a seat at the table but no one is King. No wonder then that Peck's honesty is what frightens those in his pursuit – there is no one in that time who is ready for this kind of stuff. Few are today. We all have to be somebody and from the perspective of the mind police, better a self-proclaimed lie than nothing at all.

Bergman's Dr Petersen remains a character of great interest here, for unlike her colleagues who exhibit a flair for disseminating diagnoses and pejorative labels like confetti, she refrains from such 'shorthand' – preferring to hold in view Peck's empty character as first and foremost a human being, albeit one in trouble. Avoiding all the favoured gems in cinema's psychiatric lexicon she is thus highly unusual amongst the pantheon of psychiatrists who have peopled the world of film. When one pans back from the detailed misapprehension of psychoanalysis in 1940s America, a cultural and ideological project of the time to elevate psychiatry as a healing art in the face of challenges posed by escalating numbers of psychologically scarred troops returning from the battlefields of Europe,[9] one can see a fundamental correctness in the broad brush strokes used to portray the discipline. Psychiatrists are depicted as individuals who rush to judgement, making perfunctory and damaging assessments of people on the basis of incomplete information; they occupy an elite social position, are highly concerned with their status, ally themselves with the forces of law and order and then as now favour the impersonal language of science over the intuitive wisdom of the heart. Hitchcock described *Spellbound* as 'just another manhunt story wrapped up in pseudo-psychoanalysis' (cited in Gabbard & Gabbard, 1999: 55) but given the interchangeable and contested nature of identity, the willingness to entertain the penetration of the surreal into the core of everyday normality and its lessons on power it is so much more than that. Hitchcock upholds the values that underpin conventional reality while he is visually, musically and semantically destabilising it. The film's manifest content we might say is a profound reworking of the cultural and latent political content that lies beneath its structure.

---

9. The mass psychological consequences of war have frequently shaped the development of psychiatry – and consequently the manner in which it is perceived – witness the creation of PTSD as a diagnostic category following pressure from veterans returning from the Vietnam War – evidence should it be needed that the neurobiological is political.

Peck's character, now assuming the alias of John Brown, flees to the Big Apple where he is tracked down by Petersen – a formidable achievement in itself, clearly nothing is beyond this woman. A future role in the antiterrorism squad surely beckons, or at the very least a detective series of her own. Her goals to take care of 'Brown'[10] and cure him are way beyond the boundaries of professional ethics – though well within the bounds of movie psychoanalysis. She may be professionally of a higher status but assumes the faithful subordinate position in relations between the lovers. In the blink of an eye Bergman has Peck on the couch and before you know it her brand of rapid-fire questioning has established that he is in actuality a medical doctor.

She further discerns that Brown has had a skin graft for a burn, but before the analysis can proceed further they are interrupted by delivery of the afternoon newspaper whose front page carries her picture and informs its readers that she is 'believed [to be] aiding madman wanted in Edwardes mystery'. Fearing she has been recognised by the bellboy the couple must flee, their ensuing disjointed flight to evade their pursuers flowing with the narrative consistency of a dream. When Peck later recalls his visions of the previous night to Petersen and her mentor Dr Bruloff,[11] self-proclaimed as 'one of the biggest brains in psychiatry', what we have in effect is a dream within a dream – the basis for Christopher Nolan's 2010 thriller *Inception*. *Spellbound* thus paints a picture of reality as ultimately elusive, as nested infinitely within itself, and like identity pulling itself up by its own bootstraps (Hofstadter, 1980). Bruloff expounds his version of determinism to Petersen and his vision of the 'cure'. As Petersen's lover is in his eyes 'dangerous', 'not responsible' for his actions, a 'schizophrenic' and 'certain[ly]' a murderer, Bruloff drugs him[12] with enough bromide to 'knock out three horses' and is ready to turn him in to the police. There may be confusion in the public perception of psychiatry as to whether its principal weapon against psychological turmoil really is talking and listening, but Hitchcock's film repeatedly notes that at a moment's notice those who dispense psychoanalysis are ready to turn to drugs and the guardians of the state – evidently having little real faith in what they peddle. Petersen, casting aside her 'bundles of inhibition', fiercely admonishes her one-time mentor: 'You don't know this man. You know only science. You know his mind but you don't know

10. Perhaps a lugubrious pleasure rooted in some unresolved childhood conflict of hers! Her former training analyst Bruloff later chastises her for engaging in 'Baby Talk'.

11. Bruloff, a walking, talking, bespectacled caricature of a Viennese psychiatrist, announces upon his arrival that he has just been delivering a lecture at an Army hospital. Perhaps he was deliberating on Freud's views of the death instinct – which the armed forces of the West have done so much to publicise!

12. Without his permission needless to say.

his heart.' Was psychiatry ever interested in knowing the heart? Far from being a 'schoolgirl ... operating on the lowest level of the intellect' as Bruloff retorts, Petersen is an astute mature woman prepared unlike her male colleagues to think outside the limitations of her professional training and to use her resources as a human being to deal with the situation. The master could learn from his former student were he open to it. Slapped by Bruloff, Peck awakens and prompted by Bruloff, a little reluctantly recounts what he has just dreamt.

Accompanied by the unsettling pre-psychedelic sonics of the theremin,[13] Dali's imaginative sets transport us to the incessant 'anguish of [dream] space-time' (Dali, cited in Larkin, 1974: 1) that structures the landscapes of the unconscious. This is Dali's version of the subterranean caverns of the Freudian mind; an expansive gambling house, draped with curtains festooned with eyes. A man is walking around with a large pair of scissors cutting through the curtained eyes[14] as Peck's character is seated at a card table, followed by a woman 'with hardly anything on ... walking around the gambling room kissing everybody', beginning at Peck's table. We are informed by Bruloff that the presence of this woman 'who looked a little like Constance' represents 'plain ordinary wishful dreaming'. However the Freudian take on the origins of dreams was that they were instigated by *infantile* not contemporary adult wishes. But as Freud himself in the several hundred pages of his *Interpretation of Dreams* also failed to give a single instance of a dream being traced back to an infantile wish (Foulkes, 1978) perhaps Bruloff can be forgiven.

The recollection of the dream continues with Peck dealing a large card (the seven of clubs) to a bearded man seated across the expanse of a large table. The man replies 'that makes twenty-one, I win', but on turning over his cards reveals them to be nothing but blanks. The faceless proprietor enters and accuses the bearded man of cheating and threatens him. The next scene conveys us to a wrecked landscape of Dalian motifs – crumbling buildings, juxtaposed with a gigantic leaning statuesque head mingle with the smooth emptiness of a featureless towering building from whose chimney the sprawling roots of a tree seek to claim back nature's place. The man with the beard falls from the sloping roof of the tower 'he went over slowly with his feet in the air', shadowed by the faceless masked proprietor holding what appears to be a somewhat eroticised phallic-shaped wheel which he then drops, its potential significance underscored by the zooming camera. Another scene transition and against the horizons of a shadowed geometrical world the solitary figure of Peck

---

13. Used to startling musical effect in the Beach Boys' hit 'Good Vibrations'.
14. A reference to Dali's first film *Un Chien Andalou*, notorious for its sequence in which a razor cuts through an eye.

is being chased down a slope, a colossal pair of beating wings in pursuit overhead.

Following the recollection of his dream, Peck's anxiety grows at the sight of the snow outside. This leads to a cascading series of interpretations by Bruloff and Petersen; the sloping roof symbolises a mountainside, the bearded man, Edwardes, who had plunged over the mountainside while skiing, the winged figure pursuing him is Petersen herself – 'an angel' if she grew wings in Bruloff's eyes, all of which leads them to identify 'Gabriel Valley' as the primal scene of Peck's recent amnesia. With the police hot on their heels they take a train to the named ski resort.

Petersen's air of Zen Mastery is again evident as we find the pair downhill skiing in unerringly close proximity. Such is her ease on the slopes that she would probably command a place in the Swedish Winter Olympic team. Peck too combines his trademark startled expression with an indication that some of Bergman's Buddhist aura has rubbed off on him. While of an equivalent level of skill he would however no doubt be excised from the US team on psychiatric grounds! As they approach the end of the ski run and a vertiginous cliff edge looms ahead the memories come flooding back. Peck's character recalls a childhood accident in which careering down a sloping wall he impaled his brother on a set of railings. He remembers his name – John Ballantyne; that he had been discharged from the army as a result of a plane crash and had met Edwardes whilst recuperating. Edwardes had invited him skiing and, he recalls, had plunged over the edge of the mountain some 50ft in front of him. All seems resolved with the couple heading for marital bliss until the arrival of three detectives who announce that Edwardes' body has been found at the spot suggested by Ballantyne's recall but with a bullet in the back. With Ballantyne arrested for murder and thrown in the slammer Petersen's attempts to save him from penal servitude on the grounds of 'mental distress' are given short shrift.[15] All that is left is for her is to pledge to fight for his freedom – an activity one does not usually associate with psychiatrists.

The climax to the tale occurs back in homely Green Manors as Bruloff consoles a bereft Petersen. Murchison appears offering his help and in the course of a mundane conversation admits to not having liked Edwardes, although he 'knew him only slightly'. Petersen's flash-fire mind gets to work at once, re-examining her notes of Ballantyne's dream. Laden with insight and a touch of anxiety she returns to Murchison's office to discuss it further. Murchison inextricably participates in his own downfall by duly interpreting the first part of the dream – 'the scantily clad girl', the

---

15. Further study of the cinematic use of the insanity plea is awaited!

'gambling house', the 'eyes painted on the curtains around the walls' – all symbolic renditions of Green Manors, and the details of the card game as a reference to the '21 Club' in New York. The 'angry proprietor who threatened [the bearded man] Dr Edwardes', Murchison confesses rather unnecessarily is himself. Petersen now joins the dots for the audience – the wheel dropped on the roof by the figure of the proprietor is nothing less than a revolver. Happiness for Murchison it seems was a 'warm gun'. Voilà, the 'love-smitten analyst' and 'dream detective', has unearthed the murder weapon and the motive. Murchison, in the midst of a breakdown, had accused Edwardes of stealing his job, threatened him and then shot him from behind a tree on the snowy slopes. Her work done she leaves Murchison's office to call the police and secure her happy future whereupon Murchison, with some impressive manual dexterity, courtesy of Hitchcock's fixed camera, turns the gun upon himself and blows his brains out. Death is preferable to incarceration, not a thought that had occurred to him in relation to any of his patients.

Concluding comments
Though fantasy should never blind us to the real it may often bind us to it. The insertion of the dream sequence into the film is pivotal to the plot, the film's pedagogical psychoanalytic mission and the resolution of the mystery. The plot may have been 'too complicated 'as Hitchcock saw it, but nevertheless *Spellbound* is a classic lesson from him in how the domain of the real extends beyond the boundaries of waking thought. In stretching the intellectual horizons of the audience thus, he serves up a cinematic cocktail of the therapeutic possibilities of psychoanalysis and the eternal mysteries of the human mind. But the story need not end with the movie analysts' decoding of Ballantyne's dream work. There is in fact more to it than Bruloff, Petersen or Murchison can fathom. Truffaut may have considered *Spellbound* 'weak on fantasy' (Truffaut, 1985: 165) but in classic Freudian style the dream we are given is overdetermined and Dali has inserted much more than the script can contend with. His 'desert of the surreal' not only anticipates Baudrillaud's 'desert of the real' by some years and reveals them to be but one and the same – a hyper-real simulated world, more real than real – but also finds beneath the cool rational exterior of the psychoanalytic edifice the decaying emblems of psychological modernity. Within the extensive panorama bequeathed by Dali's 'all-seeing eye' the rationality of organised psychoanalysis is a hoax. It is a lie unto itself. The bearded man – a simulacrum of Freud – resembles none other than Bruloff, who like Edwardes is a cheat; they are all playing a game, one notable feature of which is surveillance – Peck has everyone's eyes upon him – little wonder he is trying to escape. Bruloff remarks to Petersen that 'the human being very often doesn't want to

know the truth about himself and makes himself sicker trying to forget'. This is of course also true of psychoanalytic psychiatrists. A level of surrealism beyond Dali's contained contribution would be necessary for the analysts at the Green Manors 'country club' to realise the truth about themselves. Such reflexive self-awareness in the cinema's dramatis personae would have to await the further surrealist machinations of Buñuel, though Dali was not beyond a little self-revelation in what was attributed to the mind of John Ballantyne.

In the original plans for his input Dali had envisaged a statue cracking open like an egg to reveal a myriad of ants crawling over the figure of Bergman. Referencing the themes of his own 'Metamorphosis of Narcissus'[16] Dali could very well have been intending to present Bergman as the obsessed figure of Peck's rapturous love emerging from the death of Edwardes. But as Dali commonly used ants to represent his sexual anxieties as well as death this scenario may have also been a response to the arousal of his own sexual fears by Bergman's beauty. What we got instead was an alternate representation of this love – again associated with death – as the man (symbolising Edwardes, whose identity Peck's character has taken) falls from the roof in a physical trajectory which is literally 'head over heels'. Peck's 'man with no name' may be identifying with this figure not merely as one who has fallen in love, but as someone who has an appointment with death – a man whose self is being chased and 'slowly' murdered by his encounter with psychiatry. After all, was Murchison not happy to see Ballantyne, an innocent man, arrested for murder and possibly sent to the electric chair? Ballantyne in his dreams may thus foresee not just the murder of this soul but also his physical extermination as a consequence of his encounter with the mad doctors. Little wonder he looks worried.

Bergman's sweet doctor may have been represented with wings but casting her shadow over the winter slopes she is a dark angel. The dropped eroticised wheel – the revolver as it is interpreted in the film can also be read as an expression of one of Dali's obsessive preoccupations – the flaccid penis (Ballard, 1974) and a suggestion that Murchison's motive for murder may have been more than the Hollywood production code of the day could countenance. In a reversal of the oedipal myth it is the older man who fears symbolic castration from his younger vibrant counterpart. One wonders what we might get were this picture being made today? Dali's paranoiac-critical landscapes would of course be rendered in effusive 3-D hyper-reality and with the Spanish maestro's penchant for publicity, we could enjoy as a bonus total subjective immersion in the

16. Dali showed Freud this work when they met in London in 1938. Freud was intrigued (Martinez-Herrera, Alcantara & Garcia-Fernandez, 2003).

digital reality that is *Spellbound* the game! Thus with delicious Freudian irony and Dalian perversity we have a succession of dream images suffused with ambiguity – including perhaps Dali's own toward the psychoanalytic movement – the surrealists had at best an ambiguous relationship with the movement whose portrayal of the unconscious had given them so much inspiration.[17] These negate the happy-ever-after ending of Selznick's melodrama and allude to a more uncertain future in a kingdom where reason does not rule and love does not conquer all – in short a future in our world, where fantasy and reality eclipse one another and *'freedom is only possible on the basis of a certain fundamental alienation'* (Zizek, 1992: 142).

---

17. See for example LA REVOLUTION SURRÉALISTE (1984) and Littlewood (1986).

Chapter Eight

Conclusion: Psychiatry, terrorism and reality

Everyone's worried about stopping terrorism. Well there's a really easy way: Stop participating in it.

Noam Chomsky (2003: 141)

The films considered in this book do not purport to be an exhaustive survey of cinematic psychiatry. However in the range of issues upon which these films touch: the treatment of women, ethnic minorities, young people and working people, voluntary and involuntary psychiatric 'treatment', the relationship between psychiatric and legal authorities, psychoanalysis and biological psychiatry, fictional storylines and those based upon the lives of actual people, as well as the time span covered (a period of over 60 years), it can be argued that they do provide a representative coverage of how the cinema treats the psychiatric presence. The following discussion highlights what I believe are the most challenging issues to emerge from this analysis, one which has been concerned first and foremost with addressing how the practice of real psychiatry relates to its representational cousin.

Psychiatry and terrorism

A number of the films examined in these pages demonstrate that a cinema duly devoted to truth telling need show no restraint in presenting psychiatry as a source of violence and terror – exercised in the interest of maintaining the current moral and social order. The idea that psychiatry be considered a form of terrorism rests not on hyperbole but on a straightforward reading of a widely accepted definition of terrorism – the use or threatened use of force against civilian populations for political purposes (Patel, 2007: 75). Using Szasz's maxim that psychiatry be defined on the basis of what psychiatrists actually *do* rather than what they say they do – the two definitions converge. Simply put, psychiatrists use or threaten to use ECT, drugs, 'psychosurgery' or involuntary hospitalisation against people for political purposes, i.e. social control, protection of embarrassed governing elites or regimes and enhancement of their own political power. It is a measure of psychiatry's success in dispensing propaganda that this proposition may at first seem outlandish. However, it is readily apparent in numerous accounts relayed by psychiatric survivors. It is also very much evident on the big screen – from Dr Cawley's involvement with the security services (*Shutter Island*) to psychiatric collusion with police corruption (*Changeling*) and the many instances of psychiatric punishment dispensed to unwilling recipients (*Changeling, One Flew Over the Cuckoo's Nest, An Angel at My Table, A Beautiful Mind*). This is a fit close enough to support the conclusion, and just as terrorist activity is a moral–political problem (not a psychological one) so too is psychiatry with both terrorism (in its most frequent form) and psychiatric terror wielded as instruments of state power.

The world we inhabit is suffused with inverted values and distorted language designed to sustain the current regimes of terror by providing propaganda and cover for the use of force. Psychiatry is the Trojan horse in the symbolic order (Zizek, 2006a), a terrorist organisation akin to a 'moral' army no different in principle from all the other armies which proclaim themselves to be 'the most moral … in the world' (Levy, 2010: ix) and whose usual practices often bring destruction and death in the name of peace and security. The common denominators between these 'armies' are numerous and worth listing: invasion of space, use of force, destruction of liberty, violation of human rights, damage and destruction of human beings, a benevolent self-image, Orwellian language (words that 'ease the work of killing' (ibid: 108), and a manufactured social history to cover past atrocities. These can all be found in the essential dark practices of psychiatry as much as in the actions of the Anglo-American invaders in the Middle East. A knowledge which until now we have been too afraid to know stares us in the face as we munch their popcorn and drink their Coca Cola, consuming and imbibing a social reality constructed by others from ulterior motives. How has this reality managed to evade our critical awareness thus far? To answer this we must turn to the question of ideology.

Psychiatry and ideology

The purpose of this project has been to examine the depiction of psychiatry and psychiatric power in one particular and popular art form – the cinema. If we follow John Berger's maxim that the 'art of any period serves the ideological interests of the ruling class' (Berger, 1972: 68) then we might expect big-screen psychiatry to reflect and embody a set of power relations which nurture and support elite interests. We live in an era in which the nature of human existence has been re-engineered by the productive, consumptive, creative and destructive possibilities of contemporary capitalism. The reification of human life and experience as consumer products, chiefly for the entertainment industry,[1] in tandem

---

1. Including and especially the 'adult' entertainment industry (see Roberts et al., 2010).

with the publicity machine which underpins the marketing of materialism, stipulates that people continually transform themselves in synchrony and in sympathy with the prevailing gamut of false desires and manufactured wants. Psychiatry as a discipline and practice is an aid to this process – ready at a moment's notice, should the social and economic programming fail, to step in and return us to consumptive docility and obedience, the current benchmarks of normality. Because of this inherent function psychiatry should be considered an adjunct to state and pharmaceutical corporate power and an integral component of the military–industrial complex.

As a consequence of the ideological linkage between art and society, Hollywood can more readily imagine the end of the world – a sublimation of the impending threats to the capitalist order – than it can imagine the demise and abolition of psychiatry – a possibility outside the realms of permissible or even imaginable critical thought. A corollary of this impossibility of absence extends to the mode of the psychiatric appearance on film. The very idea of a trainee, someone not yet formally identified as psychiatrically qualified (empowered) is also absent from any narrative i.e. psychiatric power even when it is subjectively realised is presented as a given rather than an act of becoming. The liberal humanitarian objection to psychiatric authority in its use of 'treatments' to bring about enforced obedience to prevailing norms is, however, within acceptable bounds. Taking the foreground in the cinematic depiction of unwanted treatment is shock therapy – whether induced by electricity or insulin. Many of the films reviewed (*A Beautiful Mind*, *An Angel at My Table*, *One Flew Over the Cuckoo's Nest* and *Changeling*) contain illustrative examples of this, and all are stories set one or two generations into the past. This potentially allows contemporary psychiatry to don its modernist hat and distance itself from 'past' abuses. It is also true, however, that in turning to the past the presentation of earlier forms of shock (e.g. unmodified ECT) make transparent the essentially physically brutal nature of the 'therapy' and its use as a 'managerial procedure' in comparison to contemporary sedated and therefore 'disguised' forms (ECT with muscle relaxant plus anaesthesia).

The overwhelming impression, conveyed through both narrative and imaginal structure,[2] is that the 'therapeutic' actions are not actually therapeutic but punitive. The overt and background representation of lobotomy and its effects (see for example *An Angel at My Table*, *One Flew Over the Cuckoo's Nest*, *Shutter Island* and *Changeling*) similarly speaks to an attack on the physical and psychological integrity of persons in the name of controlling them – to render them less troublesome and more

---

2. What may be referred to as the *mise-en-scène*.

manageable to the authorities. These relations appear indicative of psychiatry as a discipline. Accordingly the images of psychiatric control at our disposal direct attention to the discipline as a prototypical form of managerialism – the disciple of the money markets in late capitalism's swan song.

Control and punishment – the key practices of the modern state identified by Foucault (Rabinow, 1991), have been nurtured in tandem with a growing fervour since the birth of psychiatry. Its overarching presence is now most keenly felt when summoned as an 'emergency' intervention, to 'calm' discordant social relations – that is in any given setting where they are judged to be in a state of sufficient unrest as to undermine established authority. The ideological function of psychiatry in short is to uphold and protect existing structures of power in society. Allied to this is the maintenance of the moral order which accompanies the status quo.

Psychiatry, science and the moral order
As argued above, the cinematic rendering of psychiatric power contains ample evidence of its quintessential role in maintaining stability in the established order. Psychiatric order thus necessarily involves a restating (or if necessary a redrawing) of the incumbent moral order, an exercise in manufacturing values not facts. As a result revealing psychiatry as a de facto moral guardian (of the state) entails a simultaneous unmasking of its pretensions to science. Noted for its self-proclaimed desires for objectivity, replicability and universality of knowledge, science would not have enjoyed the success it has if all along it had sought to divide the universe into distinct moral categories each worthy of a different class or domain of explanation. We note in nuclear physics for example, that the same fundamental processes explain equally well both sunlight and weapons-grade plutonium, one a cause of joy, the other unlimited dread. In contrast psychiatric 'science' assumes the moral order it polices is grounded in neuropharmacology, anatomy and genetics and posits quite different explanations for what is considered morally praiseworthy (e.g. the deliberate taking of life in war – considered heroic) and morally repugnant (the deliberate taking of life in civil society – considered as murder/manslaughter, even if attributed to 'diminished responsibility'.)

Psychiatric diagnoses then are invariably moral judgements disguised as medical ones. Even more disturbing however is that the continued expansion of psychiatric 'jurisprudence' into every facet of life denotes a fundamental loathing of the human condition. As almost everyone is now judged to be psychiatrically deficient in one way or another – a rather distasteful form of egalitarianism if ever there was one – we are all, by virtue of this 'imperfect' condition, considered fair game for psychiatric transformation. This process is only made possible by the public acceptance of the basic tenets of psychiatry, a widespread internalisation of the notion that human beings are biomedical machines and nothing more.

Ron Howard's treatment of John Nash's story provides an interesting example of the levels of distortion of psychiatric 'knowledge' required to achieve such a general understanding. The fact that people by and large resent being treated as if they were machines and frequently object to interventions (to correct their 'malfunctioning') which are directed at a purely physical level is somewhat paradoxical given the acceptance afforded the biomedical model in lay culture. Psychologically speaking, or more precisely psychoanalytically speaking, this evidences a splitting in how psychiatry is received by the masses – an acceptance that 'science' has 'proven' 'mental illnesses' to be brain diseases but a rejection of the professional/institutional consequences for themselves of this belief. Failure to reject this fundamental psychiatric axiom is the first step on a not-so-long march from internalised moral deficiency to technically engineered ecstasy – courtesy of the genetic, chemical or surgical warriors whose works will produce the citizens of tomorrow in a Brave New World. Such 'ecstasy' is not so much a state of euphoric happiness as blissful ignorance (for the state) marching to the drumbeat of economic efficiency. The splitting present in the appraisal of psychiatry's scientific basis and its social and personal consequences is by no means the only one present.

Psychiatric duality: Good doc, bad doc

While several of the films examined reveal Hollywood in critical mode, it has not been entirely successful in rejecting the image of medics as caregivers and caretakers of the soul. Visions of the good doctor suffuse the cinematic social landscape (*Spellbound, Donnie Darko* and *A Beautiful Mind* for example) and whilst psychiatric brutality may even on these occasions be somewhat discrete – when it is not we are instructed to deny the evidence of our senses – acts of rough treatment and violence through denial being transformed into their opposite, the alienists' own unique brand of tough love. Torture and punishment thus become a different modality of love. In seeking to explain this disavowal there are obvious dangers in extrapolating from personal to political denial (Cohen, 2001) – there is for instance no psyche to defend. It may be instructive to make the journey in the opposite direction – from the political to the personal. What is being defended politically is not the unity or integrity of the self but the power of the organisation. The coupling of terror with love is not so much unique to psychiatry as a regular feature of all political despotism, and most politics is after all despotism in practice. And why should this be so?

Zizek (2010: 99) throws some light on the matter: 'in politics, love is invoked precisely when another [democratic] legitimization is lacking.' The power to destroy has always provoked an embrace between fear and awe – with a degree of erotic charge often to be found in the latter – no doubt to appease the killing instinct. Sex and death, as Freud understood well, may reside in close proximity. Having made one's bed people invariably lie in it – even when it turns out to be a coffin.

In organisational matters, it is not so much self-esteem that directly matters but the esteem of others. The paradoxical (good versus evil; good doc, bad doc) representations of psychiatry reside in the minds of others outside the profession – those subject to psychiatric power. Note in passing that McMurphy (*One Flew Over the Cuckoo's Nest*) and Christine Collins (*Changeling*) inspire regard in others because of their unflinching courage in challenging psychiatric power irrespective of whether (like John Nash or Janet Frame) they actually survive it in some sense. The dual representations thus begin in the society at large and become internalised through their distribution and exchange across various social barriers and landscapes. This does not make psychoanalysis obsolete – rather society (or any form of social organisation) replaces the psyche as the prime subject of analysis. Concepts of defence: introjection, projection, denial, repression etc., thus remain pertinent though they must be understood as referencing primarily social (and perhaps economic) operations rather than purely intrapsychic ones.[3] Having said that, the multiple realities existing in the social world with regard to the reception of psychiatry then become subject to interpretation by individuals – and only then where such multiple realities co-exist in the same person are we correct to speak of psychoanalysis proper as the appropriate method of analysis. Inconsistency and duality however may reign across all levels.

As we have seen, big-screen psychiatry as well as its 'live' counterpart can present overt violence as love. The psychiatric duality repressed in Ron Howard's film – wherein we see John Nash physically and chemically tortured but allegedly restored to mathematical sanity by means of it, provides a compelling example of psycho-celluloid defences at work. In dressing up Nash's torture as benign we may ask on whose behalf are the filmmakers constructing this elaborate defence? Howard may wish to support his own personal view that psychiatric intervention is beneficial and in so doing he may be aided by the extensive industry propaganda. He may be influenced by his own prior role in the workings of the mental health system in relation to friends and family – which may be anything

---

3. In his discussion of 'Geopsychoanalysis' Jacques Derrida considers the failure of political discourse to date to integrate the 'axiomatics of a possible psychoanalysis' (Derrida, 2007: 330). See also Roberts, 2007.

from guilt inducing to self-rewarding, and then there is the author of his screenplay whose mother works in the mental health professions. The matter of where the film's finance comes from may also be of relevance. Executives may wince at the possible adverse reactions a critical portrayal may attract from powerful industry sponsors – the dollar often being the bottom line. It is no coincidence that the least ambiguous of the films discussed in these pages – where psychiatry is seen naked from the waist down as it were began life as independent productions. Thus Howard and his co-worker's personal motivations, alongside existing social representations of mental illness and pharmaceutical efficacy coalesce with power and money to bring about what is in effect a psycho-celluloid reaction formation – violence reinterpreted as love. Like the dream, the joke or the hysterical symptom, the film too has its own latent work underpinning the determination of the final product.

With the above in mind it is instructive to compare *A Beautiful Mind* with Scorsese's *Shutter Island* fantasy and Forman's *Cuckoo's Nest*. With Scorsese we are treated to psychiatric noir as ideological retreat. The insights flowing from Forman's 1970s critique of the mental health system have by the first decade of the twenty-first century evaporated from Ron Howard's work and are in retreat from Scorsese's.

The resurrection of institutional psychiatry over this time is, it has to be admitted, a deft conjuring trick. The restoration of psychiatric defences since the 1970s, however impressive, is nevertheless incomplete. The primary processes of psychiatric reason deliver Teddy Daniels to insanity but not before he has delivered a scathing critique of psychiatric practices. If it takes the audience the best part of two hours to be convinced of his insanity – and a good many of the audience are not convinced of that – then this ought to at least stimulate some thought as to the nature of the path on which psychiatry walks. The defences against this realisation however run through the thoughts of auteur, actors and audience alike. It is almost as if the character is trying to escape from the confines of fiction and convince the people who created him that what he has to say is true. Ben Kingsley who played Dr Cawley described the erstwhile doctor as one who radiates 'unconditional love'. At the film's dénouement this is an individual who consents to the lobotomy of one of those he supposedly 'loves'. It appears to have undergone the same kind of transformation as witnessed in *A Beautiful Mind*. Such psychiatric 'love' if it occurs anywhere on the spectrum of human emotion would have to be characterised as jealous and vengeful i.e. not as love at all. In Scorsese's historical dream, it is not so much that the maestro denies the reality of psychiatric violence but that he appears to be unable to unambiguously accept it. These opposing strands of thought appear in the guise of the 'good' English (Cawley) and 'bad' German (Naehring) doctors, mapping the West's great myth of good and evil from World War II onto the trajectory of post-war psychiatry. Beneath any myth however, all is not what it seems and in *Shutter Island* we have a film in which very little is what it seems. In resolving the apparent psychiatric conflict between benevolent and malevolent psychiatry through the finale of Teddy Daniels' lobotomy, Scorsese's art house piece may constitute an admission that the management of the 'mad', from its historical roots to the present, has at its core a black and cruel heart. *Shutter Island* purports to gives us psychiatry as it enters the modern age, but this is misleading. Pre-modern, modern and postmodern psychiatry swallowed by the myth of enlightenment reason applied to the human organism is a nightmare, more likely to herald a new dark age than the futurist dream we are continually promised. Heidegger may not have had psychiatry in mind when he uttered the famous words, but on this basis the dreadful 'has already happened'. The truth is we don't want to know it – which may have been Heidegger's original point! Psychiatric belligerence is posited as both a historical relic and a necessary contemporary practice to curb the excesses of violent unreason. In this framework all 'unreason' is considered potentially violent – which is why it takes us so long to figure out Teddy Daniels' place is with the 'criminally insane'. We see little actual violence from him – but plenty of reason. On 'discovering' his insanity it is as if the audience's memory of his transparent reason has been wiped clean. But what of violent reason – the sole rights to which are monopolised by the state? The demarcation between the mad and the sane, when all is said and done, ultimately seems a matter of who has the right to threaten and manage the bodies of others.

The filmmaker's challenge, in daring to hold a mirror to psychiatry, is to second-guess for how long the audience (and film crew) can sustain the gaze. Each production is a veritable showdown for cinematic revelation. If the gaze is averted or the blindfold remains in place the result is a film which replicates the sin of psychiatry, refusing or failing to recognise that the lawlessness which the psychiatric marshals have come to control also resides in the men (and women) with the badge. It is the perennial question in the surveillance society and it has been with us a long time – who watches the watchers? The problem of keeping the true nature of psychiatry before the lens therefore goes to the roots of what it means to run a society on democratic lines. The social contract depends on the governed consenting to be governed for the benefits of political order. Szasz rightly fears the function of psychiatry in a therapeutic state in which the freedom to give such consent is predicated on the notion of 'good' 'mental health'. Psychiatry, as the Nazis and Soviets well understood, is a useful weapon in the fight against democracy. 'The worst possible system ... excepting all others' it may be, as Churchill said, but it is fragile, and will slide into one incomparably worse if current trends continue. The task facing the cinema of psychiatry is to stare into the mirror long enough that the fear of petrification dissolves. Psychiatrists, like Medusa, live in fear of their own reflection. The irrationality they discover everywhere is a reflection of their own, a grand projection which year on year traps ever more people in the psychiatric zoo. A confused population in awe of the psychiatric profession have part internalised the aura of projected benevolence which surrounds them. It sits side by side with the fear which is also provoked – as good an example of splitting as one could hope to find in the psychoanalytic literature, and it is this which is more often than not projected onto the screen. One may hope that should the profession take a closer look at this phenomenon, it will eventually, like the serpent, swallow its own tail – a distinct improvement on the current state of affairs in which psychiatry's illegitimate incursions into scientific territory are nothing but charlatanry. The result of this is that in scientific eyes rather than swallowing its own tail it has disappeared up its own intellectual behind.

A further recurring motif in cinema's portrayal of 'mad' doctors and which could be considered a subordinate aspect of the good-doc, bad-doc complex concerns their tendency to be economical with the truth. The recipe here is the bad pretending to be good under cover of mendacity, a sliver of benevolence, and a thinly concealed layer of authority. Thus we have lies about the nature of medication purportedly being given (*Donnie Darko*), about the supposed beneficial consequences of lobotomy (*An Angel at My Table*), or drugs (*Cuckoo's Nest*) or even what the problems facing the person in the patient role actually are (*Changeling, Cuckoo's Nest* etc.). These cinematic scenarios could have been drawn directly from the real world. The duplicity has certainly not escaped critics (e.g. Szasz, 2008), though its frequent presence in film shows that awareness of this outside professional and academic circles is far more extensive than the profession would like to acknowledge. Of course the structure of this opposition between 'good' and 'bad' doctor is very different to the good cop, bad cop dichotomy. Implicit in the film/TV rendition of police partners is a cooperative interrogation stratagem agreed between buddies in which the identity of each resides in their common purpose which is to reveal the criminal secret. There is no real good or bad cop – each is an image intended to deceive, projected into the mind of the suspect. The alternative psychiatric identities in contrast compete for the claims of the real. They fight for the truth of one another – the 'good' seeking to affirm itself by denying, destroying or hiding the bad, the unnameable other. The 'bad' however seeks to reveal the other and to reveal it as a lie. It is only in the image of the bad that the nature of psychiatry is fully revealed. The good doc, bad doc pair is therefore an antagonistic one.

There is some mileage in the delineation of the 'good' doctor as attentive, listening, caring – psychoanalytic in posture, while the bad is delineated by an overtly, medical, biological disposition. However any representation of psychiatry as benign and which rests on this opposition is deceptive. Modern psychiatry is biological, for it there is no search for meaning, no ghost (of morality) in the machine. The basic tenets of psychoanalysis as growth through talking and structured interpersonal interaction belong nowhere in medicine (Szasz, 1988). Psychiatrists in many of these films wear their attentive, humanistic credentials on their sleeves (*Donnie Darko, Shutter Island, Cuckoo's Nest, A Beautiful Mind*), but these are quickly wiped – to be supplanted or accompanied by the usual array of drugs, deceit and medical torture with which it is hoped to end the peculiar search for meaning that the subject is engaged with. As long as psychoanalysis in any shape or form posits itself as belonging within the family of medicine, a Faustian pact for the social power and control which medicine delivers, it is making of itself a hostage to fortune.

Memory and cinema as resistance
Zizek (2006b) remarked that cinema does not tell us what to desire but how to desire – and in that spirit it can be said to instruct us in how to desire psychiatry, or whether to desire it at all. Whatever licence has been taken in the telling of various stories, the visual rendering of psychiatric intervention as assault is essentially accurate and truthful – if accuracy and truthfulness are decided on the basis of 'patient' accounts rather than the numerical advantage of those in opposition to them (doctors, police, social workers, family members) at the time of their subjugation and initiation into the patient/prisoner role. The good psychiatrist on screen can be envisaged as a defence against the unpleasant realisations stirred by the deeds of his or her unholy counterpart. Given the extensive efforts devoted to convincing the public of the benevolence and utility of psychiatric intervention, the cinema being but one of several vehicles for this, it behoves one to think that the psychiatric lady 'doth protest too much'. The necessity for dramatic elaboration of feigned goodness, reminiscent of Freud's 'return of the repressed', reaches its peak in the depiction of psychoanalytic psychiatrists.[4] Ingrid Bergman's Dr Petersen is not only protecting the identity of her patient – she is also fearful of her own unmasking as bogus doctor and healer of the soul. The transference here runs deeper than even Freud might have wanted.

The wall constructed around the image of psychiatry is not there merely to satisfy the present-day 'consumer' of psychiatric image and

---

4. Alternatively, an explanation of this inversion of the moral status of the image need not rely on the notion of repression at all. Intentional deception, a well-known feature of advertising, will do the trick just as well.

reality. The defence is also simultaneously both historically and politically situated – how else could the medical profession have wrested control of the asylums unless they had first masqueraded as beneficent? The split and the mask have always been there. Our response to this defence must be to unmask the brutality which lies behind the mask – to destroy the professional false self and make known that which it doesn't want us to know. This is psychoanalysis with a sword – its aim, the disintegration of psychiatric reality. European rather than British or American cinema has arguably been the boldest in this respect. The Swedish films based on Stieg Larsson's bestselling millennium trilogy[5] paint an unflattering portrait of state-controlled psychiatry, allied to the cover-up of a series of racist murders and rapes perpetrated by a clandestine group of sadistic Nazis, former Soviets and assorted sex traffickers. The symbolic resonances with the profession's murky past and hidden history of association with the darkest forces of European history are uncompromising and clear. The attempt to discredit the revelations of child-abuse victim and kick-boxing punk Lisbeth Salander by psychiatric slander ultimately fail – and in so doing reveal the nature of the psychiatric gambit for what it is – an attempt to dominate the symbolic order and define reality by force. Salander's mining of the hidden past thereby earns her an altogether different fate to that one meted out by Hollywood to Teddy Daniels for his excavations into historical truth.

The perpetual defensive strategies employed in the presentation of mental health care allude to the fact that we are both witness to and participants in a battle royal. One of the conclusions to be drawn from the current analysis is that despite the ambiguities present in a variety of works, the cinema constitutes an important bulwark of resistance in this battle, erecting barriers against the misinformation which surrounds the history, nature and purpose of psychiatric practice. This conclusion draws our attention to a key function of the cinema of psychiatry, which is to act as a repository of social memory, detailing the abuses perpetrated by psychiatrists throughout the age in the name of doing good. This explains (at least in part) why the wards, consulting rooms and operating theatres of the big screen are historically situated. Over time psychiatric power has multiplied. By returning to the past we can see a lesser, perhaps purer form of the beast. It is relatively free of its modern-day defences though no less the creature of habit that polices the streets of present-day thought in the guise of the cruel superego of the nation state. In the here and now we must face a plethora of representations resulting from the media-led,

---

5. *The Girl with the Dragon Tattoo, The Girl Who Played with Fire, The Girl Who Kicked the Hornet's Nest.*

drug-company sponsored, professionally promoted, fear-inducing propaganda[6] which throws an illusory veil over reality, exacerbating the 'threat' posed by the 'mentally ill' and exonerating the good psychiatrists who are tasked with bringing them to reason and order. It is a distasteful, though heroic task once the premise behind it has been accepted.

The historical dimension to psychiatric representation notwithstanding, it remains the case that the window on psychiatric time found in the cinema is a narrow one, predicated upon the precepts of modernism. Whilst the manner and mode of representation is capable of challenging psychiatry's pretensions to enlightened development, cinema remains in a historical impasse. A more savage critique of psychiatry as conventional wisdom may be afforded were cinema to peer out from these cosy confines and gaze upon a fledgling psychiatry in the pre-modern era. Alternatively it could advance to the very recent past to examine the intertwining of professional and personal motivations in psychiatrist executioners of the modern age – Radovan Karadzic, for example, self-styled healer and architect of genocide in Bosnia (Roberts, Becirevic & Paul, 2011). Beyond the boundaries which mark the straightjacket of conventional criticism lies the psychiatrist as killer as well as captor.

The cinema is important not only for its twin contributions to entertainment and economic life but also because it is a vehicle for knowledge and communication. As such it comprises a significant avenue to explore in our search for meaning in the world. As with other forms of 'text' however, the meanings that can be read from its products are not transparent. One must learn to decode, deconstruct and read what comes out on film. If one opens one's eyes though the writing is on the wall – writing that begins on a prescription pad and ends in a prison cell – imaginatively, cognitively and in the real. The moving hand having written will then move on – but will we? If we are not careful we may wake up duly reformed as perfect psychiatric zombies who have learned to love Big Pharma, the IMF and the World Bank. Cured of any impulse to resistance our impending existential demise would accompany the burial of all essential freedoms.

Resistance however is not futile. Psychiatry can be rejected. However first it must be understood and approached from its given place in the social structure. Individual critiques are of considerable value – and there have been a good many of them – but the possible readings of the psychiatric presence in the world will carry more weight and power if the challenges to current practices which they inform proceed on a social rather than an individual basis. The psychiatric juggernaut which thunders over the length and breadth of the human landscape can only be

---

6. This is the production routine of psychiatry as Pepsi Cola.

effectively halted if the action against it is informed, systematic, organised and collectively based. Cinema has a potentially important role to play in this, not only in shattering our shared illusions of illness and cure but also in cultivating and disseminating a critical picture to masses of people of exactly what it is we are up against when we collide with psychiatric power. Such art would nourish the view, expressed by Muhsam (cited in Osser, 1980: xi), that human creativity 'free of authority and external compulsion' is rooted in a 'longing for liberation from coercion'. If psychiatry is to go the way of the wind, the power of the image can be utilised to build that freedom and point the way to a world still to win.

References

Abella, A. (2008) *Soldiers of Reason: The RAND Corporation and the rise of the American Empire*. Orlando, FL: Houghton Mifflin Harcourt.

American Psychiatric Association (1994) *Diagnostic and Statistical Manual of Mental Disorders* (4th ed. rev.). Washington, DC: American Psychiatric Association.

Bakan, J. (2005) *The Corporation. The pathological pursuit of power and profit.* London: Robinson Publishing.

Ballard, J.G. (1974) Introduction. In D. Larkin (Ed.) *Dali.* London: Pan Books.

Bannister, D. & Fransella, F. (1971) *Inquiring Man. The theory of personal constructs.* Harmondsworth: Penguin.

Bateson, G. (Ed.) (1961) *Perceval's Narrative: A patient's account of his psychosis 1830–1832.* Palo Alto, CA: Stanford University Press.

Baudrillard, J. (1994) *Simulacra and Simulation.* Ann Arbor, MI: University of Michigan Press.

Baudrillard, J. (1996) *The Perfect Crime.* London: Verso.

Beeding, F. (2002) *The House of Dr Edwardes.* New York: Rosetta Books. (Original work published 1927)

Bentall, R.P. (2009) *Doctoring the Mind.* London: Allen Lane.

Berger, J. (1972) *Ways of Seeing.* London: BBC and Penguin Books.

Bhugra, D. (2006) Severe mental illness across cultures. *Acta Psychiatrica Scandinavica, 113,* suppl. 429, 17–23.

Bloom, H. (Ed.) (2008) *Bloom's Modern Critical Interpretations: Ken Kesey's One Flew Over the Cuckoo's Nest.* New York. Infobase Publishing.

Bourne, H. (1953) The insulin myth. *The Lancet, 265,* 1259.

Boyle, M. (1990) *Schizophrenia: A scientific delusion?* London: Routledge.

Bracken, P. (1986) Psychiatry and Surrealism. *Bulletin of the Royal College of Psychiatrists, 10,* 80–1.

Brown, D. (1991) *Bury My Heart at Wounded Knee: An Indian history of the American West.* London: Vintage. Original work published 1970.

Buñuel, L. (1994) *My Last Breath.* London: Vintage.

Burr, V. & Butt, T. (2000) Psychological distress and postmodern thought. In D. Fee (Ed.) *Pathology and the Postmodern* (pp. 186–206). London: Sage.

Bush, G. (1990) *Presidential Proclamation 6158.* July 17th. http://www.loc.gov/loc/brain/proclaim.html Accessed May 2010.

Byrne, R. (2009) Screening Madness. A century of negative movie stereotypes of mental illness. Time to change. *Mind.* http://www.mind.org.uk/campaigns_and_issues/report_and_resources/1439_screening_madness Accessed May 2010.

Campion, J. (2010). Introduction. In J. Frame, *An Angel at My Table*. London: Virago Press.

Cardeña, E., Lynn, S.J. & Krippner, S. (2000) *Varieties of Anomalous Experience*. Washington, DC: American Psychological Association.

Chomsky, N. (2003). *Power and Terror: Post 9/11 talks and interviews*. New York: Seven Stories Press.

Chomsky, N. (2010) *Hopes and Prospects*. London: Hamish Hamilton.

Cohen, S. (1985) *Visions of Social Control*. Cambridge: Polity Press.

Cohen, S. (2001) *States of Denial*. Cambridge: Polity Press.

Coleman, A. (1982) *Game Theory and Experimental Games: The study of strategic interaction*. Oxford: Pergamon Press.

Connerton, P. (2009) *How Modernity Forgets*. Cambridge: Cambridge University Press.

Cooper, D. (1976) *The Grammar of Living*. Harmondsworth: Pelican.

Cornwell, R. (2010) *Living the American dream. But all the time spying for Russia*. http://www.independent.co.uk/news/world/americas/living-the-american-dream-but-all-the-time-spying-for-russia-2014110.html Accessed June 30th 2010.

Cox, D. (2010) Hollywood's mental block. *The Guardian. Film and Music*. Friday 23rd July.

Curtis, A. (1995) *The Living Dead: Three films about the power of the past*. London: BBC.

Curtis, A. (2007) *The Trap: What happened to our dream of freedom?* London: BBC.

Curtis, M. (2003) *Web of Deceit: Britain's real role in the world*. London: Random House.

Curtis, M. (2004) *Unpeople: Britain's secret human rights abuses*. London: Random House.

Dali, S. (2007) *The Diary of a Genius*. Washington, DC: Solar Books.

David, A.S. (1999) On the impossibility of defining delusions. *Philosophy, Psychiatry and Psychology*, 6 (1), 17–20.

Davis, J. (2008). How *Changeling* changed J. Michael Straczynski. *Creative Screenwriting Magazine* (Creative Screenwriters Group), 15 (5), 18–21.

Dawkins, R. (2006) *The God Delusion*. London: Bantam.

Day, J., Bentall, R.P., Roberts, C., Randall, F., Rogers, A., Cattell, D., Healy, D., Rae, P., & Power, C. (2005) Attitudes toward antipsychotic medication. *Archives of General Psychiatry*, 62 (7), 717–24.

Derrida, J. (2007) *Psyche: Inventions of the other. Volume 1*. Palo Alto, CA: Stanford University Press.

De Vries, M. (no date) Review of *Asylums* (Erving Goffman). *MeTZelf. Association for Medical and Therapeutic Self-Determination*. http://metzelf.info/Book%20Reviews/Asylums.html Accessed July 16th 2010.

El Hai, J. (2005) *The Lobotomist*. Hoboken, NJ: John Wiley.

Faggen, R. (2002) Introduction. In K. Kesey, *One Flew Over the Cuckoo's Nest* (pp. ix–xxii). London: Penguin.

Fernando, S. (2003) *Cultural Diversity, Mental Health and Psychiatry: The struggle against racism*. London: Routledge.

Fernando, S., Ndegwa, D. & Wilson, M. (1998) *Forensic Psychiatry, Race and Culture*. London: Routledge.

Flacco, A. & Clark, J. (2009) *The Road out of Hell. Sanford Clark and the true story of the Wineville murders*. New York: Union Square.

Foulkes, D. (1978) *A Grammar of Dreams*. Sussex: The Harvester Press.

Frame, J. (2009) *Faces in the Water*. London: Virago Press.

Frame, J. (2010) *An Angel at My Table*. London: Virago Press.

French, S. (1996) *The Terminator*. BFI modern classics. London: British Film Institute.

Gabbard, G.O. & Gabbard, K. (1999) *Psychiatry and the Cinema* (2nd ed.). London: American Psychiatric Press.

Goffman, E. (1961) *Asylums: Essays on the social situation of mental patients and other inmates*. New York: Doubleday.

Green, B. (2007) Psychiatry in the cinema. *Psychiatry Online* http://priory.com/psych/psycinema.htm Accessed July 2010.

Greene, G. (2001) *The Heart of the Matter*. London: Vintage. Original work published 1948.

Gregory, R. (1966) *Eye and Brain: The psychology of seeing*. London: Weidenfeld & Nicolson.

Harper, D. (2007) The complicity of psychology in the security state. In R. Roberts (Ed.) *Just War: Psychology and terrorism* (pp. 15–45). Ross-on-Wye. PCCS Books.

Henri, A., McGough, R. & Patten, B. (1974) *The Mersey Sound*. Harmondsworth: Penguin.

Hofstadter, D. (1980) *Gödel, Escher, Bach: An eternal golden braid*. Harmondsworth: Penguin.

Illich, I. (1977) *Limits to Medicine*. London: Pelican.

Jansson, B. (1998) *Controversial Psychosurgery Resulted in a Nobel Prize*. NobelPrize.org. The official website of the Nobel Prize. http://www.nobelprize.org/nobel_prizes/medicine/laureates/1949/moniz-article.html Accessed June 2010.

Jenkins, R. (2009) Mother of six Houria Chentouf hid terror manual in burka. *The Times*, November 3rd. http://www.timesonline.co.uk/tol/news/uk/crime/article6899548.ece Accessed September 2010.

Jones, M. (Ed.) (2005) Introduction. In R.F. Scott, *Journals, Captain Scott's Last Expedition*. Oxford: Oxford University Press.

Kaldor, M. (2001) *New and Old Wars: Organised violence in a global era*. Cambridge: Polity Press.

Kaufman, K. & New, C. (2004) *Co-Counselling: The theory and practice of re-evaluation co-counselling*. Hove: Bruner-Routledge.

Kelly, R. (2003) *The Donnie Darko Book*. London: Faber & Faber.

Kendrick, J. (1929) Northcott baffled. Court denies his insanity plea. *Los Angeles Times,* January 3rd. http://latimesblogs.latimes.com/ thedailymirror/files/1929_0103_cover.jpg Accessed September 2010.

Kesey, K. (2002) *One Flew Over the Cuckoo's Nest*. London: Viking Penguin.

Klein, N. (2007) *The Shock Doctrine*. London: Allen Lane.

Komiya, N., Good, G.E. & Sherrod, N.B. (2000) Emotional openness as a predictor of college students' attitudes toward seeking psychological help. *Journal of Counseling Psychology, 47* (1), 138–43.

Kuhn, H. & Nasar, S. (2001) *The Essential John Nash*. Princeton, NJ: Princeton University Press.

Laing, R.D. (1965) *The Divided Self*. Harmondsworth: Pelican Books.

Laing, R.D. (1967) *The Politics of Experience and The Bird of Paradise*. London: Penguin.

LA REVOLUTION SURRÉALISTE (1984) An historical vignette: Surrealism and anti-psychiatry. *Bulletin of the Royal College of Psychiatrists, 8,* 175.

Larkin, D. (Ed.) (1974) *Dali*. London: Pan Books.

Lasby, C.G. (1975) *Project Paperclip: German scientists and the Cold War*. New York: Atheneum.

Lehane, D. (2003) *Shutter Island*. London: Bantam.

Lehane, D. (2010) *Dennis Lehane (Shutter Island) Interview*. YouTube. http:// www.youtube.com/watch?v=T6-yaCVM6to Accessed May 2010.

Levy, G. (2010) *The Punishment of Gaza*. London: Verso.

Lifton, R.J. (2000) *The Nazi Doctors*. New York: Basic Books.

Littlewood, R. (1986) Psychiatry and surrealism. *Bulletin of the Royal College of Psychiatrists, 10,* 191, July.

Littlewood, R. & Lipsedge, M. (1997) *Aliens and Alienists* (3rd ed.). London: Routledge.

Liu, J.H. & Hilton, D.J. (2005) How the past weighs on the present: Social representations of history and their role in identity politics. *British Journal of Social Psychology, 44,* 537–56.

Ludwig, M. (1995) *The Price of Greatness*. New York: Guilford Press.

Mantel, H. (2009) Introduction. In J. Frame *Faces in the Water* (pp. vii–xiv). London: Virago Press.

Marcuse, H. (1964) *One-Dimensional Man: Studies in the ideology of advanced industrial society*. Boston: Beacon.

Marsh, J. (Director) (2008) *Man on Wire*. Icon Home Entertainment.

Martinez-Herrera, J., Alcantara, A.G. & Garcia-Fernandez, L. (2003) Dali (1904–1989): Psychoanalysis and pictorial surrealism. *American Journal of Psychiatry, 160* (5), 855–6.

Marx, K. (2006) *The Eighteenth Brumaire of Louis Bonaparte*. Champaign, IL: Standard Publications. (Original work published 1852)

Masson, J. (1990) *Against Therapy*. London: Fontana.

Milgram, S. (1974) *Obedience to Authority*. London: Tavistock.

Mngxitama, A., Alexander, A. & Gibson, N.C. (Eds.) (2008) *Biko Lives! Contesting the legacies of Steve Biko.* New York: Palgrave MacMillan.

Moncrieff, J. (2008) *The Myth of the Chemical Cure.* Houndmills: Palgrave.

Mosher, L.R. (1998) *Resignation letter from the American Psychiatric Association.* http://www.moshersoteria.com/articles/resignation-from-apa/. Accessed July 2010.

Nasar, S. (1998) *A Beautiful Mind.* New York: Touchstone.

Nasar, S. (2007) Introduction. In H. Kuhn & S. Nasar (Eds.) *The Essential John Nash* (pp. xi–xxv). Princeton, NJ: Princeton University Press.

Nash, J. (2007) Autobiography. In H. Kuhn, & S. Nasar, S. (Eds.) *The Essential John Nash,* (pp. 5–11). Princeton, NJ: Princeton University Press.

New Zealand Health Information Service (NZHIS) (2002) *Public Hospital Discharges for Psychiatric Somatotherapy (ECT) 1995–2000.* Wellington. Ministry of Health.

Noyes, A.P. & Kolb, L.C. (1958) *Modern Clinical Psychiatry.* Philadelphia: Saunders.

Orwell, G. (1946) *Politics and the English Language.* http://www.mtholyoke.edu/acad/intrel/orwell46.htm. Accessed June 2009.

Osser, M. (1980) *Anarchism in the Dramas of Ernst Toller.* New York: University of New York Press.

Pais, A. (1982) *Subtle is the Lord: The science and the life of Albert Einstein.* Oxford: Oxford University Press.

Parks, R. (2000) *Voodoo Science.* Oxford: Oxford University Press.

Patel, N. (2007) Torture, psychology and the 'war on terror': A human rights framework. In R. Roberts (Ed.) *Just War: Psychology and terrorism* (pp. 74–108). Ross-on-Wye: PCCS Books.

Paul, J.J. (2008) *Nothing is Strange with You: The life and crimes of Gordon Stewart Northcott.* Bloomington, IN: Xlibris.

Petit, P. (2002) *To Reach the Clouds.* London: Faber & Faber.

Popper, K.R. (2002) *The Open Society and Its Enemies. Vol 1.* London: Routledge.

Porter, R. (2003) *Madness: A brief history.* Oxford: Oxford University Press.

Rabinow, P. (Ed.) (1991) *The Foucault Reader.* Harmondsworth: Penguin.

Rasmussen, C. (1999) The boy who vanished – and his impostor. *Los Angeles Times,* February 7th. http://articles.latimes.com/1999/feb/07/local/me-5769 Accessed September 2010.

Read, J. (2004a) A history of madness. In J. Read, L.R. Mosher & R. P. Bentall (Eds.) *Models of Madness,* (pp. 9–201). London: Routledge.

Read, J. (2004b) Electroconvulsive therapy. In J. Read, L.R. Mosher & R. P. Bentall (Eds.) *Models of Madness,* (pp. 85–100). London: Routledge.

Read, J. & Masson, J. (2004) Genetics, eugenics and mass murder. In J. Read, L. R. Mosher & R.P. Bentall (Eds.) *Models of Madness* (pp. 35–42). London: Routledge.

Read, J. & Reynolds, J. (1996) *Speaking our Minds. An anthology of personal experiences of distress and its consequences.* Houndmills: Palgrave.

Rees, L. (2005) *The Nazis: A warning from history.* London: BBC Books.

Reich, W. (1974) *Listen, Little Man!* New York: Farrar, Straus & Giroux.

Roberts, R. (2007) Power, illusion and control. In R. Roberts (Ed.) *Just War: Psychology and terrorism,* (pp. 160–9). Ross-on-Wye: PCCS Books.

Roberts, R. (2010) Looking back: Madness, myth and medicine. *The Psychologist, 23* (8), 694–5.

Roberts, R. (2011) Psychology at the end of the world: Mind and behaviour in the Antarctic. *The Psychologist, 24* (1), 22–5.

Roberts, R., Becirevic, E. & Paul, S. (2011) Truth and denial: Psychological perspectives on reconciliation in Bosnia. In J. Elford (Ed.) *Just Reconciliation* (pp. 129–46). Oxford: Peter Lang.

Roberts, R., Sanders, T., Smith, D. & Myers, E. (2010) Participation in sex work: Students' views. *Sex Education: Sexuality, society and learning, 10* (2), 145–56.

Rogers, C.R. (1957) The necessary and sufficient conditions of therapeutic personality change. *Journal of Consulting Psychology, 21,* 95–103.

Rosenhan, D. (1973) On being sane in insane places. *Science, 179,* 250–8.

Rothenberg, M. (2003) *Children with Emerald Eyes.* Lyons, CO: North Atlantic Books.

Russell, A.J., Munro, J.C., Jones, P.B., Hemsley, D.R. & Murray, R.M. (1997) Schizophrenia and the myth of intellectual decline. *American Journal of Psychiatry 154* (5), 635–9.

Sereny, G. (2001) *The German Trauma: Experiences and recollections 1938–2001.* London: Penguin.

Slater, T.S. (2008) One Flew Over the Cuckoo's Nest; A tale of two decades. In H. Bloom (Ed.) *Bloom's Modern Critical Interpretations. Ken Kesey's One Flew Over the Cuckoo's Nest* (pp. 123–35). New York: Infobase Publishing.

Smail, D. (2005) *Power, Interest and Psychology: Elements of a social materialist understanding of distress.* Ross-on-Wye: PCCS Books.

Soros, G. (2010) *The Soros Lectures at the Central European University.* New York: PublicAffairs.

Szasz, T. (1983) *Ideology and Insanity: Essays on the psychiatric dehumanization of man.* London: Marion Boyars.

Szasz, T. (1988) *The Ethics of Psychoanalysis: The theory and method of autonomous psychotherapy.* New York: Syracuse University Press. (Original work published 1965)

Szasz, T. (2007a) *Coercion as Cure: A critical history of psychiatry.* New Jersey: Transaction Publishers.

Szasz, T. (2007b) Diagnoses are not diseases. In T. Szasz, *The Medicalization of Everyday Life,* (pp. 27–36). New York: Syracuse University Press.

Szasz, T. (2007c) Psychiatry's war on criminal responsibility. In T. Szasz, *The*

Medicalization of Everyday Life, (pp. 102–16). New York: Syracuse University Press.

Szasz, T. (2008) *Psychiatry: The science of lies*. New York: Syracuse University Press.

Todorov, T. (2003) *Hope and Memory: Reflections on the twentieth century*. London: Atlantic Books.

Townsend, L., Floersch, J. & Findling, R.L. (2009) Adolescent attitudes toward psychiatric medication: The utility of the Drug Attitude Inventory. *Journal of Child Psychology and Psychiatry, 50* (12), 1523–31.

Truffaut, F. (1985) *Hitchcock: A definitive study of Alfred Hitchcock*. London: Simon & Schuster.

United States Government (1949) *Trials of War Criminals before the Nuremberg Military Tribunals under Control Council Law, 10,* 2, 181–2. Washington, D.C. U.S. Government Printing Office, 1949. Available Online: National Institutes of Health http://ohsr.od.nih.gov/guidelines/nuremberg.html. Accessed June 2010.

Vidal-Barrantes, N. (2004) Creativity and madness revisited from current psychological perspectives. *Journal of Consciousness Studies, 11* (3–4), 58–78.

Voltarie (1947) *Candide*. Harmondsworth: Penguin Classics. Original work published 1588.

Von Neumann, J. & Morgenstern, O. (2007) *Theory of Games and Economic Behavior* (Commemorative Edition). Princeton, NJ: Princeton University Press.

Vulliamy, E. (1994) *Seasons in Hell: Understanding Bosnia's war*. London: Simon & Schuster.

Wachowski, L. & Wachowski, A. (1999) *The Matrix*. Village Roadshow Films, Warner Bros.

Walsh, J. (2007) Is there a link between madness and creativity? *The Independent*, 18th March. http://www.independent.co.uk/life-style/health-and-families/health-news/is-there-a-link-between-madness-and-creativity-440374.html Accessed August 2010.

Whitaker, R. (2002) *Mad in America*. New York: Basic Books.

Wing, L. (1981) Asperger's syndrome: A clinical account. *Psychological Medicine, 11* (1), 115–29.

Yeats, W.B. (1982) *Collected Poems*. London: MacMillan.

Zizek, S. (1992) *Looking Awry*. Cambridge, MA: MIT Press.

Zizek, S. (2006a) *How to Read Lacan*. London: Granta Books.

Zizek, S. (2006b) *The Pervert's Guide to the Cinema*. Lone Star: Mischief Films.

Zizek, S. (2010) *Living in the End Times*. London: Verso.

Appendix

Ten Points of the Nuremberg Code
(US Government, 1949)

1. The voluntary consent of the human subject is absolutely essential.
    This means that the person involved should have legal capacity to give
    consent; should be so situated as to be able to exercise free power of
    choice, without the intervention of any element of force, fraud, deceit,
    duress, over-reaching, or other ulterior form of constraint or coercion;
    and should have sufficient knowledge and comprehension of the
    elements of the subject matter involved as to enable him to make an
    understanding and enlightened decision. This latter element requires
    that before the acceptance of an affirmative decision by the
    experimental subject there should be made known to him the nature,
    duration, and purpose of the experiment; the method and means by
    which it is to be conducted; all inconveniences and hazards reasonable
    to be expected; and the effects upon his health or person which may
    possibly come from his participation in the experiment.

    The duty and responsibility for ascertaining the quality of the
    consent rests upon each individual who initiates, directs or engages in
    the experiment. It is a personal duty and responsibility which may not
    be delegated to another with impunity.

2. The experiment should be such as to yield fruitful results for the good
    of society, unprocurable by other methods or means of study, and not
    random and unnecessary in nature.

3. The experiment should be so designed and based on the results of
    animal experimentation and a knowledge of the natural history of the
    disease or other problem under study that the anticipated results will
    justify the performance of the experiment.

4. The experiment should be so conducted as to avoid all unnecessary
    physical and mental suffering and injury.

5. No experiment should be conducted where there is an a priori reason
    to believe that death or disabling injury will occur; except, perhaps, in

those experiments where the experimental physicians also serve as subjects.

6. The degree of risk to be taken should never exceed that determined by the humanitarian importance of the problem to be solved by the experiment.

7. Proper preparations should be made and adequate facilities provided to protect the experimental subject against even remote possibilities of injury, disability, or death.

8. The experiment should be conducted only by scientifically qualified persons. The highest degree of skill and care should be required through all stages of the experiment of those who conduct or engage in the experiment.

9. During the course of the experiment the human subject should be at liberty to bring the experiment to an end if he has reached the physical or mental state where continuation of the experiment seems to him to be impossible.

10. During the course of the experiment the scientist in charge must be prepared to terminate the experiment at any stage, if he has probable cause to believe, in the exercise of the good faith, superior skill and careful judgment required of him that a continuation of the experiment is likely to result in injury, disability, or death to the experimental subject.

Films Reviewed

Shutter Island (pp. 1–15)
> Year of Release: 2010
> Director: Martin Scorsese
> Production: Paramount Pictures/Phoenix Pictures/Sikelia Productions/
> Appian Way

Changeling (pp. 16–28)
> Year of Release: 2008
> Director: Clint Eastwood
> Production: Universal Pictures/Imagine Entertainment/Relativity
> Media/Malpaso Productions

Donnie Darko (pp. 29–41)
> Year of Release: 2001
> Director: Richard Kelly
> Production: Metronome in association with Pandora Cinema/Flower
> Films (II)/Adam Fields Productions/Gaylord Films

A Beautiful Mind (pp. 42–55)
> Year of Release: 2001
> Director: Ron Howard
> Production: DreamWorks/Universal Pictures/SKG Imagine
> Entertainment

An Angel at My Table (pp. 56–68)
> Year of Release: 1990
> Director: Jane Campion
> Production: Hibiscus Films/New Zealand Film Commission/Television
> New Zealand/ Australian Broadcasting Corporation/Channel 4 Films

One Flew Over the Cuckoo's Nest (pp. 69–83)
> Year of Release: 1975
> Director: Milos Forman
> Production: Fantasy Films

Spellbound (pp. 84–97)
> Year of Release: 1945
> Director: Alfred Hitchcock
> Production: Selznick International Pictures/Vanguard Films

Index of Names and Subjects

PTSD (post-traumatic stress disorder)
64, 91

R
'R, Mrs' 62
Rabinow, P. 101, 115
RAND Corporation 43, 48, 49, 72
Rasmussen, C. 17, 115
'Ratched, Nurse'/'Big Nurse' x, 70, 72,
    75, 76, 77, 80, 81, 82, 83
Read, J. ix, 5, 21, 63, 115
reality 19, 35, 44, 48, 98, 99
    and economics 44
    escape from 89
    psychiatric vii, 12, 35, 38, 108
    social xi, 28
    submerged viii
Rees, L. 5, 115
Reeves, Keanu 72
Reich, W. 81, 116
religion 41, 81
religious iconography 39
REM sleep deprivation 57
repression 103
Reynolds, J. 21, 116
Richter, Max 6
Riemann hypothesis 49
Ritalin 37
Roberts, R. 26, 29, 57, 99, 103, 109, 116
Rogers, C.R. 36, 116
'Rosen, Dr' (fictional) 47, 52, 53
Rosen, Dr J. (real) 47
Rosenhan, D. 10, 116
Ross, Katharine 29, 39
Rothenberg, M. 54, 116
Russell, A.J. 1, 33, 116
Russell, Bertrand 48
Russell–Einstein manifesto 1

S
'Salander, Lisbeth' 108
Sampson, Will 71
San Quentin prison 25
Sarajevo 1

Saunders, Hilary 84
science, junk 81
schizophrenia 25, 33, 37, 52, 54, 61, 64,
    66, 92
    degenerative 53
    genetic predisposition to 54
Schwarzenegger, Arnold 30, 39
science and the moral order 101–2
scientific
    delusion 61
    reason 74
Scorsese, Martin viii, 12, 104, 105, 120
Scott, Ridley 14
Seacliff Hospital 60, 61
SEATO pact 49, 50
Second World War xi, 45 (see also
    World War II)
'Sefelt' 75
Selznick, David O. 84, 85, 86, 97
Sereny, Gitta 4, 15, 116
sex and death 103
sexual
    abuse of patients 47
    activity, abnormal 24
Sexy Beast 3
Shakespeare, William 66
Shutter Island viii, xi, 1ff, 21, 28, 55, 67,
    69, 84, 99, 100, 104, 105, 107, 120
Slater, T.S. 72, 78, 116
Smail, D. 87, 116
'Smith, Winston' 12
social
    control xi, 13, 25, 28, 34, 98, 107
    IQ 43
    order viii, ix, 87, 98
    memory of psychiatry ix, 108
    power, centres of 20
    responsibility 45
Social Security payment 67
'Solando, Rachel' 1, 3, 4, 6, 8, 9, 10, 11,
    14, 21
Soros, G. 81, 116
Soviet Union 43, 48
Soviets 1, 2, 105, 108

Fiction's Madness

Liam Clarke

ISBN 978 1 906254 23 0, 2009
£18.99 (£18.00 direct, p&p free in the UK)

Fiction can be a powerful adjunct to mental health education and practice, its capacity to clarify and enlighten aspects of the field beyond doubt. With a rare gift for making the scholarly accessible, Liam Clarke presents an original interpretation of mental health issues based on some of the greatest works of English fiction. Utilising plays and novels, as well as a wide range of critical sources, he provides many fascinating and provocative insights into human distress, its effects and consequences both past and present. If we seek to encounter people and not to decode them, so must we look at ourselves from whatever perspectives we can. This groundbreaking book makes a fine contribution to an enterprise that is as necessary as it is enjoyable and rewarding.

> 'This is a book of immense power. It deploys all the devices that literature is capable of to press its case, to argue forcibly and persuasively for the humanising of psychiatry … It is a book that demonstrates how fundamental to clinical practice is a familiarity with the humanities, the interpretative and critical domains of our intellectual life … The act of reading carefully prepares us to listen carefully in the clinical setting, to think and reflect, to consider and engage empathically, and to imagine the world of the Other as if it were our own.'
> *Femi Oyebode, Professor of Psychiatry, University of Birmingham*

Liam Clarke is currently Reader in Mental Health at the University of Brighton. For many years he has been involved in mental health care mainly through writing and teaching. His current research entails writing up a 'non-model' of 'ordinary decency' to account for ethical practice. In addition, he is putting the finishing touches to a manuscript which critiques ethnography and its assumptions.

PCCS BOOKS
the independent publisher for independent thinkers
www.pccs-books.co.uk

JUST WAR
PSYCHOLOGY AND
TERRORISM

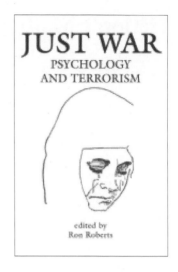

RON ROBERTS

ISBN 978 1 898 05992 9, 2007
£20.00 (£19.00 direct, p&p free in the UK)

The invasion and occupation of Iraq by US and UK forces in March 2003 set in motion a global chain of events, from the growth of terrorist networks to the curtailment of civil liberties, from which the dust has yet to settle. The war in Iraq, seen as part of the wider 'War on Terror', is perhaps a watershed for the discipline of Psychology, posing uncomfortable questions for the psychological community regarding the stance adopted towards the powerful and the privileged. This book explores perspectives on peace, conflict and protest to deconstruct the psychological and cultural processes which support the normalisation of imperial wars. It calls for a more socially responsible psychology in the 21st century, unshackled from state interests, one which places human rights firmly at its centre.

Contents
• The Complicity of Psychology in the Security State • British Psychology's Response to the Invasion and Occupation of Iraq • The War on Terror: The road from Belmarsh to Guantánamo Bay • Torture, Psychology and the 'War on Terror': A human rights framework • The Psychology of Anti-War Activism • Relational Psychology in the War Speeches of Bush and Blair: Beyond 'Us' and 'Them' • Power, Illusion and Control: Families, states and conflict • Children and War: Making sense of Iraq • Sleepwalking into Totalitarianism: Democracy, centre politics and terror • Deconstructing Terrorism: Politics, language and social representation • A Psychology for Peace?

PCCS BOOKS
the independent publisher for independent thinkers
www.pccs-books.co.uk